Checkerback's
Journey

The Migration
of the Ruddy
Turnstone

by Marjory Bartlett Sanger

CHECKERBACK'S JOURNEY
The Migration of the Ruddy Turnstone

CYPRESS COUNTRY

MANGROVE ISLAND

Checkerback's Journey

The Migration of the Ruddy Turnstone

MARJORY BARTLETT SANGER

Illustrated by Betty Fraser

THE WORLD PUBLISHING COMPANY
CLEVELAND AND NEW YORK

Published by The World Publishing Company
2231 West 110th Street, Cleveland, Ohio 44102
Published simultaneously in Canada by
Nelson, Foster & Scott Ltd.
Library of Congress catalog card number: 68–26975
Text copyright © 1969 by Marjory Bartlett Sanger
Illustrations copyright © 1969 by Betty Fraser
Designed by Jack Jaget

For Marion

Contents

"Adieu Foulard"	13
The Warm Peninsula	29
On the Sea Island	45
Carolina	61
The Outermost Beach	76
Night Flight	93
Tundra World	113
"Big Wind Comin'"	131
"Adieu Madras"	144
LIST OF ILLUSTRATIONS	151
INDEX	153

Checkerback's
Journey

The Migration
of the Ruddy
Turnstone

"*Adieu Foulard*"

THE PALE WATER lapped at the black sand with barely a ripple. As far away as the horizon the sea lay flat and glassy, reflecting the sky. On the beach the tall palms stood motionless; no wind moved their fronds. Behind them rose high green hills, brightened here and there with flowering trees like red and yellow clouds, and behind the hills a volcano looked down on the island.

The island bore the French name of Martinique, and it belonged to France although it lay in the West Indies, thousands of miles from Paris. The sea that appeared so calm this April morning was the Caribbean. The volcano was named Pelée, which means "bald one," and it too appeared calm, although there had been a day over half a century before when it had erupted with little or no warning and wiped out an entire city. That was one reason why the beach was black; the sand was mostly lava.

Onto the lava sand a stocky little cinnamon and black and white shorebird with bright orange legs suddenly dropped down and landed, and almost at once began turning over shells and bits of seaweed at the high-tide line, looking for something to eat. The day might be placid, but the bird was in a hurry. He had flown all the way from Brazil, and he still had a long journey to take.

The shorebird was a ruddy turnstone. On the northeastern shores where he fed and rested during his long journey the fishermen called him "Checkerback" because they said the black-and-white pattern

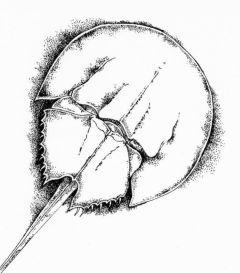

of his wings in flight made him look like a flying checkerboard.

The turnstone had another name too, its scientific name, *Arenaria interpres. Arenaria* means "sandy," or "pertaining to sand." *Interpres* means "a go-between," like our word "interpreter." Probably *Arenaria interpres* was described for his customary running back and forth along the sand between the tide lines, looking for food. His more familiar name, "turnstone," graphically depicts his habit of turning over stones and pebbles on the beaches where he searches for insects, mollusks, and crustaceans. Where there are no stones to turn, the turnstone, undaunted, will probe in seaweed or gravel or even wet sand to dig up the eggs of the horseshoe crab, each egg with a tiny perfectly formed crab inside.

This April day while Checkerback fed hungrily and the crystal-clear Caribbean water washed the black beach, a rufous-throated solitaire was whistling its slow flutelike song in the jungle forests of the nearby hills, or *mornes,* as the Martiniquais called them. On and on sang the West Indian thrush, over the huge drooping leaves of the banana plantations, over the mango trees, the bougainvilleas and hibiscus and wild orchids, as gaudily colored as the South American parrots Checkerback left behind. And all the while over the *mornes* and plantations and villages with wooden, palm-thatched huts brooded Mount Pelée, forty-five hundred feet above sea level and quiet now. Picnickers even dared to climb its slopes to eat spiny lobster in the shelter of its crater. A cloud, the first of the morning, rested for a moment on its peak, looking for all the world like a puff of smoke.

It had not been since May 1902 that the cloud shapes at the peak really were volcanic fire. Until then, St. Pierre, the seaport capital of the island, had been called "the little Paris of the Caribbean." It was undoubtedly the prettiest city in the West Indies, a pastel-colored resort spa with an opera house, cathedral, cafés, and small but elegant mansions with columned porches and sculpture. Of all of this, little was left after the sudden eruption of Pelée. They say the sole survivor among nearly thirty thousand was a prisoner condemned to death and secured safely in a cavelike cell.

Over this "Pompeii of the New World," another name for the unfortunate city, buried in ash and overgrown with vine, Checkerback took a brief flight. Beneath him, as he turned out over the water, some of the weedy ruins could still be seen: submerged courtyards and ornamented walls, mossy mosaic floors and sunken statues. The ruddy turnstone flew low and straight over them to the active harbor of Fort-de-France, the new capital.

Along a stone breakwater he walked purposefully, hopping up on bits of rope and shell, stopping now and then to poke at a crevice for a bit of bait left by an early morning fisherman. Below

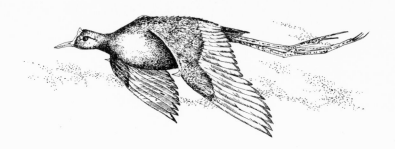

the breakwater, on an island schooner bound for Guadeloupe, a sailor was stacking kegs of native rum and softly singing an old Martiniquais chant of farewell, "Adieu foulard, Adieu madras." Legend says that the song was written too hundred years ago by an old-country governor of the island when he heard that he was being called back to France.

Tall, honey-skinned girls, who walked barefoot and in the manner of the Carib Indians from whom they were descended, no longer wore the traditional tied madras headdress of their mothers. They listened to the sailor's song with a sad smile. Even before the volcano had buried St. Pierre, the island had been known as *"Le pays des revenants,"* the land of ghosts.

One of those ghosts who must surely return to haunt a homeland that, in spite of the excitement of her life in France, she always loved best is the Empress Josephine. Rose Joséphine Tascher de la Pagérie was born at Les Trois Islets, across the bay from Fort-de-France. The dreaming Creole girl left Martinique for Paris and became the bride of Napoleon Bonaparte. There for a little while she reigned as empress of all the French. Now her weathered statue stands in the Savane, an untended and weedy square in the new capital. The statue gives the impression of something that has been left behind by mistake, and the eyes are looking across the palm trees toward Les Trois Islets.

Checkerback was not concerned with history. No longer hungry for the moment, he joined a flock of shorebirds on the beach at the edge of the harbor.

Shorebirds make up that group that we most associate with beaches. Who may not have spent a summer afternoon watching sanderlings darting just where the foam washes up on the damp shingle, probing close to the water's edge for coquinas and periwinkles, and never seeming to get wet? And who may not, on a spring morning, have listened to the distinctive plaintive call of a black-bellied plover as it stood solitary, its back to the sea?

Gulls and terns, even though also associated with our shores, do not belong to the group called shorebirds. Neither do the geese and ducks of our wetlands or the water-loving waders—herons and egrets and ibis. Plovers and sandpipers are perhaps the best known to us of all the shorebirds, but there are many others in this large transoceanic family. Jaçanas, oyster catchers, avocets, stilts, dowitchers, knots, willits, and phalaropes are only a few. And then, of course, there are the turnstones.

The black turnstone, *Arenaria melanocephala,* is the vigorous and abundant turnstone of the Pacific coast where it frequents the rockweed-draped or barnacle-crusted ledges of the offshore islands, often venturing out into the surf for its meal of mussels and snails. It annoys West Coast fishermen by pecking at the salmon laid out

17

on racks to dry in the sun. About the same size as its eastern cousin, it is, as its name indicates, much darker, appearing sooty black at a distance. When it flies, though, it shows much the same spectacular checkerboard wing pattern.

Arenaria interpres, the ruddy, also occurs in Europe where it is known simply as the turnstone. In France it is called *tourne-pierre,* in Germany *steinwälzer.*

But Checkerback, for all his travels, had not been to the Pacific coast nor to the shores of Europe. He did not know any other turnstones except those that he traveled with on his migrations or met in his Brazilian wintering grounds or his Arctic breeding grounds or in between.

Most shorebirds have fairly long legs for what wading they have to do. Well-named stilts bend gracefully from a comparatively great height and catch the insects they enjoy from the surface of the water. Shorebirds also have strong bills for probing in sand and rockweed and pebbles. Their feathers tend to be mostly brown or gray or white, the colors of dry and wet beaches, so that they often seem to blend protectively into their backgrounds. Plovers and turnstones are stockier than sandpipers, with shorter, thicker bills. Sandpipers are more delicately formed, with slightly longer and more slender bills and duller shading, often spotted or streaked. Most 18

shorebirds have pointed wings to help them on their long journeys.

Probably the most remarkable feature of this family is the extraordinary migration that its members embark upon twice a year between their warm, sometimes even tropical, winter homes, and their wild, often Arctic, summer breeding grounds. The birds' innate compulsion to leave their familiar shores and fly thousands of miles across open stretches of sea, over noisy ports, through wind and rain and fog, baffles the mind and stirs the imagination.

It also fascinates and preoccupies the scientist. Studies are constantly being made; research is carried out both in the field and in the laboratory. Why and when the birds go, how they find their way, their built-in powers of navigation and orientation are questions continually pondered and tested. Ever since Audubon banded his first phoebe and watched it return to its old nest the following spring, ornithologists have longed to solve the secret of the birds' long journeys.

Checkerback was moving restlessly among the shorebirds on the bottle- and net-littered beach at Fort-de-France. Sandpipers and plovers gathered and dispersed, and they too seemed anxious to be off. Sometimes a small cloud of them would rise up for no apparent reason, and, flying as one bird, wheel out over the calm sea and then settle again on the warm sand.

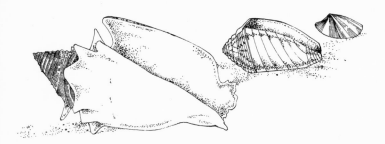

The turnstone let out a soft *kek-kek* and pushed aside the broken piece of a king conch shell. Martinique fishermen still use the whole empty shells as horns to call in the offshore fishing fleet, or to summon solitary fishers on the black beaches casting their nets into the tide. Having found nothing he wanted under the piece of shell, the bird stood for a moment as if undecided about what to do next. Alongside the other shorebirds he was, in his fresh breeding plumage, a striking sight.

The tawny chestnut-red of his mantle shone in the Caribbean light. Like a feathered bib a band of black dropped down over his shoulders and throat. His head was white with black and buff markings; his bright orange legs showed distinctly against the brownish, grayish, and flesh-colored legs of his companions. His tail was white at the base, with a black band near the end which was edged in white. Suddenly he flew a few yards to a seaweed-covered jetty, and the harlequin pattern of his back and wings flashed in the sun.

Another turnstone was feeding on a bit of shrimp he had found on the jetty. He raised his wings pugnaciously as Checkerback approached, but Checkerback did not pause to fight over the food. Instead he flew on to the wharf near where the sailor had finished loading his cargo of rum and was now tacking slowly out of the harbor, past the lighthouse and toward Josephine's Les Trois Islets. 20

Martinique was discovered by Columbus on his last voyage, in 1502. When he tried to make a landing, however, he was driven away by the fierce and handsome Carib Indians who had called their island Madinina, which meant "island of flowers." It was not until well over one hundred years later that a European colony was established there; this was accomplished by the French in 1635. Adventurous young noblemen raised sugar cane on great slave-worked plantations, and built for their pleasure the city of St. Pierre. Before the eruption of Pelée, many fashionable Parisians sailed away from their winter snow and rain to spend the season in the sun of Martinique, taking healthful baths at the spa and enjoying the balls and theaters of this most civilized capital of the West Indies. All that delight, as we know, came to an abrupt end exactly four hundred years from the time of Columbus' discovery and rebuff.

Hot noon lay over the harbor. The brown sails of the interisland sloops hung slack while the crews huddled in what little shade there was and ate their lunch of *colombo,* an Indian dish of meat and rice, or Creole-spiced crayfish. A slab of fresh pineapple and a bowl of straw-colored raw sugar waited on an enginehouse roof. To it fluttered a fearless black, white, and yellow bird, a bananaquit, the size of a sparrow and called *sucrier* by the natives. The ban-anaquit ignored the pineapple, sweet though it was and oozing in

the sun. Instead it grabbed a beakful of sugar. The "sugar bird" was well named.

Overhead a white-tailed tropic-bird, pelagic ranger of the open ocean, suddenly appeared, its long central tail feathers streaming out behind. It hovered for a moment, then folded its wings and dropped downward in a steep plunge, twisting just as it hit the water. Up it came with a flying fish in its coral-red bill. A frigate-bird, lazily riding the thermals, observed the dive and lunged out in pursuit. The tropic-bird swirled and dodged and barely made its escape, flapping its wings like a big pigeon and passing over the same black beach where Checkerback had landed that morning.

Frigate-birds, named for the pirate ships and also called man-o'-wars, obtain much of their food by robbing, or pirating, other sea birds. If they fish for themselves their feathers become heavy and waterlogged; they are in danger of drowning. Pirating is their means of survival.

Along the sand below the tropic-bird, sea-grape trees spread out their gnarled trunks and their large leathery leaves. When flattened by hurricane winds, these resilient trees will continue to grow, prone on the beaches, until the trunks are able to raise themselves again. And the leaves, at least on the islands where the Spanish explorers landed, were used, it is said, as pages for the conquistador's records.

Here and there behind the sea grapes flourished the notorious manchineel, aptly called by the natives "the poison tree." Its milky sap can produce a bad rash; even rain falling from the pointed leaves can irritate the skin. Rumors say that twigs of the manchineel, tossed into the water, will bring fish to the surface in such a stunned condition that it is easy to catch them in one's hands. There is another rumor that conquistadors, falling alseep in the shade of the poison tree, never awoke!

Untroubled by the dangers of poison, land birds this April afternoon were singing and feeding in the thickets. The black-whiskered vireo, Martinique's *père gris,* "gray father," doubtless because of the whiskerlike markings, the rufous-headed yellow warbler, or *petite jaune,* and a small brownish flycatcher called *siffleur* because of its shrill whistle were all heard by Checkerback as he foraged here and there.

Halfway up a hill stood one of the island's many crumbling sugar mills, vestiges of the days when young Frenchmen crossed the ocean to make a fortune in cane. Now the mill had been almost taken over by a grove of *arbres à la pluie,* reclaiming the land. The name, translated "rain trees," is thought by some to have arisen because of the myriads of insects that flock to its leaves and twigs, sucking the fragrant juice and then squirting it out like a shower of raindrops. Also, in an evening shower, the sensitive upper leaves,

like our acacia or mimosa, fold at dusk, allowing more rain to sink into the grass below than the usual broad-leaved tropical trees. On some of the drier islands of the Caribbean, rain trees have even been planted to induce precipitation.

Beside a pink powder-puff bloom, a pearly-eyed thrasher peered out and saw a variety of jewel-toned iridescent hummingbirds come to the blossoms. In the whole of the continental eastern United States there is but one hummingbird, the ruby-throat; it is astonishing therefore to observe in the tropics as many as ten species hovering around a single tree.

Under this particular *arbre à la pluie* lurked one of the deadliest snakes in the world, the dreaded *fer-de-lance,* or spearhead, named for its lance-shaped head and also for the way it will throw itself from a branch like a javelin to destroy its prey. In Central America it is called *barba amarilla,* or yellow beard, because of its yellowish chin and throat.

Very few islands harbor this menace, and no one is exactly sure how and why the snake reached Martinique. Legend says that it was imported to the island to discourage the slaves from leaving the plantations and running away through the jungle. It seems more logical to believe that it arrived on hurricane logs, great trees from the South and Central American mainland, broken by storms and swept out to sea by storm tides, carrying their captive, involuntary

25

passengers. Many animals and plants have reached distant shores in this way.

Mongooses from India were introduced on Martinique in an attempt to wipe out the poisonous snakes, but the mongooses multiplied so rapidly that they too became a problem, especially since they preferred chickens and their eggs to reptiles. Warmed by the April sun filtering through the leaves, the *fer-de-lance* made its way up the trunk of the rain tree and lay along an upper branch, awaiting a victim.

Up the foothills toward brooding Pelée the bright-topped flowering trees climbed. There was the jacaranda, or fern tree, with its delicate, finely cut foliage and bell-shaped, blue-violet flowers that also drew multitudinous insects. There was the pink *poui,* that the French called *poirier du pays,* not because its fruit is pear-like—it is actually a narrow seed-bearing pod—but probably because *poui* sounded to them like *poirier,* a tree they knew.

Most brilliant was the towering immortelle, with its orange clustered blossoms. There had been times when it too had been called a poison tree. Its seeds, it was rumored, when steeped to a thick lotion and that lotion smeared on an arrowhead, could kill any enemy. It is even reported that Ponce de León himself was dispatched by just such an arrow. The filtered juice of the immortelle, natives said, could cause blindness if one sat under the tree in the rain. And the broken twigs could stupefy fish. Yet in South

and Central America the flowers are bought and sold in markets to season soups and salads, and, it is claimed, to encourage sleep!

Never out of sight above this dense community of fruit and flower, insect, bird, and reptile, loomed the volcano, the "bald one," where whatever trees there were were stunted and twisted and bent low by ever-blowing winds and thwarted by infertile soil.

Checkerback's instinct now told him that it was time to move on. This was his second northern migration; he had been hatched two summers before on the Arctic tundra and he had made his way to the unfamiliar shores of Brazil. A week before his arrival at Martinique he had felt a stirring to be off, to leave his winter coastal beach. Island by island, across the equator and beyond, he had proceeded north with a group of other turnstones, and sometimes with plovers and sandpipers.

This afternoon he paced along the lava, walking faster and faster as he picked over the garlands of dried seaweed at the tide line. He recognized the need of storing food to satisfy his never-ending hunger on the long flight ahead. He might be out of sight of land for uncountable miles.

Birds' bodies have an exceptionally rapid rate of metabolism, which means that they burn up their food extremely quickly and therefore must have more readily available most of the time.

The turnstone grabbed a beetle from the windrow, and then

another. Then without a backward look at the mountain behind him or at the ruined city, bits of it still glimmering through the sunlit water he passed over, he shot like an arrow to the harbor where, on the breakwater, the fishermen were engaged in cleaning their catch. All the gulls of Fort-de-France seemed to be circling over them and screaming.

Checkerback picked up a bit of discarded bait. Two native girls walked by him. On their heads were flat circular baskets of bananas, mangoes, and pineapple, with branches of coffee leaves and blossoms laid on top to shield the fruit from the burning sun. One of the fishermen, attracted by the fragrance of the flowers, glanced up and smiled. The girls walked on without a sound.

A sudden breeze filled the loose sails of the waiting sloops. Rough-hewn booms swung over the heads of sailors in siesta. Rousing themselves, they stretched and looked at the sky, and then northward toward their destination, Guadeloupe, the other French Antillean island, with only British Dominica in between.

It was Checkerback's destination too. The ruddy turnstone raised his wings, gave a faint cry, and continued his journey.

The Warm Peninsula

HIS JOURNEY led him to the Florida Keys. Strung like beads on a chain, and bound together by bridges and a highway, most of the islands that are called the Keys curve southwestward from the marshy, open Everglades to the busy city of Key West.

The word "key" comes from the Spanish word *cayo,* meaning "little island." Ponce de León and the conquistadors who discovered them gave them their name. And it would be natural to think that Key West means westernmost island, but it does not. The Spaniards called it *Cayo Hueso,* which means "Island of Bones." They called it that because they found it strewn with the bleached bones of the Carib and Calusa Indians who had fought there. Two hundred years after the Spanish discovery, British subjects from the Bahama Islands, or Conchs as they were called because of their fondness for the meat of that large marine gastropod, translated *Cayo Hueso* to Key West. It seemed logical enough and the name remained.

On a wharf lined with shrimp boats, Checkerback was patrolling the edge of the harbor. It was an active place. The shrimp industry had brought a new prosperity to the island just at the time when it needed it most. And it all happened in a remarkable way.

Fishermen, catching a shark in their nets, found it filled with shrimp. All of a sudden it seemed that their prayers had been answered. For years the fishermen had been looking for shrimp

beds, but with no success. Over and over they cast out their nets, trawling at all locations and depths, only to draw the nets up empty. The shrimp must be there because the shark had feasted on great quantities of them. But where were they? It was all most myserious.

Then, one night, a boat returning late from a day of trawling tossed over a final net. When it was hauled in it was found to contain five hundred pounds of pink shrimp.

The fishermen rejoiced. They had finally found what they had been looking for. But the next morning, casting in the same spot, they again pulled in empty nets. The mystery seemed as baffling as ever, especially when that same night the nets were full of shrimp again.

The answer was that the pink shrimp the fishermen called "pink gold" buried themselves in the sandy bottom throughout the day and rose only at night to feed on their favorite repast, plankton, which also rose at night to feed in the dimly lit waters.

The word "plankton" comes from the Greek word for wanderers, and the tiny plants and animals that make up this plankton do indeed wander and travel far on ocean currents, sometimes floating passively and sometimes actively swimming. Like the ruddy turnstone, plankton also makes an extraordinary migration.

It is what is called a "vertical migration," that is, it moves up and down instead of north and south. At night it rises toward the faintly lit surface of the sea, sometimes climbing as much as several hundred feet, and then sinking back into the murky depths with the coming of dawn.

It is a basic rule of life that every plant and animal strives to situate itself in its most favorable environment, the one which is best suited for its survival and its successful growth and reproduction. One can assume, therefore, that plankton prefers a dimly lit environment. And there it finds *its* sustenance: microscopic one-celled diatoms and dinoflagellates, whose name means "terrible whip bearers."

Plankton, in addition to being the shrimp's favorite food, also supplies a soupy form of nourishment for countless maritime animals from worms to whales. And migrating plankton makes up a remarkably vast percentage of the number of the world's living organisms, and plays a vital role in the ecology of the sea. Feeding and being fed upon, its remains ultimately sink as gently as falling snowflakes to the pitch-dark bottom where plants cannot grow. And even there it provides a scrap of food for the depth feeders, those unseen animals that nose along the bed of the ocean, searching for something to eat.

About seventy per cent of our globe is under water. It has been suggested that nine-tenths of all our animals and plants still lead their lives in that element where life itself is believed to have begun, an element that remains relatively unfamiliar to us, the two-legged mammals who have found our most favorable environment on dry land.

What do we know about the sea? We know that we can swim in it and float on it, that it provides a highway for ships and a home for fish, and, at least until modern times, some protection for us against invading enemies. We know that the sea appears to be changeful in color and texture and motion, usually dependent upon weather conditions; yet we also know that the sea does not move significantly, except as coastlines erode or build up. Those waves that appear to push tons of water through the ocean can be compared to grasses in a windy meadow; the tops bend but the roots stay firm.

We know too that oceans do not only separate continents; they also join them and, unlike the continents, they are connected with one another as well. This tends to provide more or less uniform living conditions for their marine inhabitants. And in spite of the great numbers of plants and animals, this very uniformity limits the variety of species that live there. The land, because of its great diversity of terrain—forest and field, swamp and mountain, river and desert—has had to develop a tremendous quantity of species, each one adapted to its kind of life. Most of the amphibians, mammals, insects, and seed plants belong to dry land.

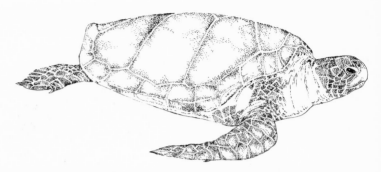

And this same tremendous quantity of species has caused a fierce competition to arise, every plant and animal fighting for a spot to put down a root, or build a nest, or dig a hole. Such competition forced many species to abandon forever their accustomed homes and move to strange, and therefore more difficult, ones. Vines moved up trees; orchids and other epiphytes, or air plants, left the earth entirely and moved into treetops. Mangroves were driven into the sea by crowding vegetation; cypresses became water-tolerant for the same reason. So did many of the marine grasses.

Whales, seals, sea turtles, and crabs have also, over innumerable years of physiological change, made successful transitions. Not all of these transitions are complete. Sea turtles still return to the dry sandy beaches to lay their eggs.

Oceanography as a science is relatively new. With conquests of the Antarctic, Mount Everest, and outer space accomplished, man is turning his attention more and more to the unexplored depths of the sea. The new science contains many old sciences: geography, geology, biology, chemistry, physics, and mathematics. Astronomy and meteorology are also involved, together with the study of currents and drifts. But although we call the science a recent one, men have been curious about the ocean since ancient times.

The Babylonians thought of the world as a kind of island surrounded by a flat ocean, bounded by sunrise and sunset. The Greeks

of the Golden Age told of Atlantis, destroyed by an earthquake overnight and sunk forever beneath the waves. Adventurous Phoenician sailors brought home stories of the weedy Sargasso Sea. Some of them traveled completely around Africa, from the Red Sea to the Pillars of Hercules, near Gibraltar.

Although we like to believe that until Columbus' voyage people believed that the world was flat and that mariners venturing too far into the ocean would fall off some sort of edge into nothingness, what is actually the truth is that the first recorded historian, Herodotus, in the fifth century B.C., described the earth as a sphere with the ocean covering a large part of it. And Ptolemy of Egypt, about five hundred years later, drew a map of a global world that became a standard.

But maps and descriptions are one thing, and actual voyages are another, and one cannot question the appraisal of John Fiske, the nineteenth-century historian, of Columbus' voyage as being "the most daring thing that had ever been done . . . the first to bid goodbye to the land and steer straight into the trackless ocean in reliance upon a scientific theory."

The man who has been called the father of oceanography was also called the "Pathfinder of the Sea." His name was Matthew Fontaine Maury and he was an officer in the United States Navy.

In 1855 he published a geography of the sea, and in it for the first time he brought together a knowledge of sun and weather, moon and tides, winds and currents, and the complex interrelationships of all of these.

A current that particularly interested Maury was the Gulf Stream. He called it a "river flowing in the ocean," and declared that nowhere else was there such a majestic flow of waters, that its speed was far faster than that of the Mississippi or Amazon, and that its volume was a thousand times as great.

It had been admired before. Ponce de León, the discoverer of Florida, met, in his questing caravels, "a current so strong that it drove them back, though they had the wind large." Later the Spanish conquistadors made use of this strong current to carry their ships bearing the Aztec treasures from Montezuma's court down the long "Spanish corridor" leading home.

Benjamin Franklin also knew of the ocean river and drafted his famous chart of the "Gulph Stream . . . a current so called which comes out of the Gulph of Florida, passing North-Easterly along the coast of America."

The Stream, as it is known to mariners, is an actual river passing through the relatively stable ocean water at speeds, in some places, of nearly five knots an hour. It races northward through the Florida Strait that it helped to carve, and is so distinctly blue in color that

it can easily be distinguished. It is also very warm; its surface heat off the Keys is about eighty degrees Fahrenheit. Where its warm water reaches colder northern air, dense fogs arise, endangering fishing vessels on the Grand Banks off Newfoundland. Yet it is the "great moderator," enabling people to live comfortably in cold latitudes. Existence in the British Isles would be very different if it were not for the Gulf Stream.

Checkerback, however, was far from the British Isles. On his journey from Brazil, through the French island of Martinique and the American island of Key West, he had landed on an island named for its first inhabitants. Checkerback's little flock of ruddy turnstones joined a group of plovers and sandpipers resting and trying to feed on the pitted gray coral beach of deserted Indian Key.

The tide was high. The birds were crowded together toward the scrub palmetto and sisal plants that covered the island. A sea wind had freshened, and the smaller sandpipers, or peeps, stood in the lee of the larger birds, facing the wind and preening their feathers, or seeming to sleep, their heads resting on their backs. Many stood on one foot, with the other tucked up beneath them. Some even hopped around on one leg.

There was not much to eat on the beach, and what there was was coated with gray sand and chalky white marl. Some of the birds washed what they found in the clear rainwater rock pools 36 that had formed here and there on the shore reflecting the sky. Checkerback took a moment from his continuing search for food to bathe in one of the pools.

The sandpipers, which had arrived together in a flock of about fifty, stayed together as they foraged and fed. They raced back and forth over the spattered coral like a grounded cloud. The black-bellied plovers, though, left their flocks and stood apart from the others, solitary figures on the beach, whistling now and then their plaintive *whee-o-wee.*

On a sudden whim, Checkerback leaped up and circled the island with his characteristic flight, quick, sometimes flapping his wings, sometimes just sailing. Half of his group joined him. Then they landed again almost exactly where they had settled before.

The most famous of bird artists had also landed on this beach. In 1832 John James Audubon, already well known, had come to study and paint the birds of this most tropical section of our land. He arrived on the revenue cutter *Marion,* and everything was done to make his journey a pleasant one.

He had not cared much for the northern part of the warm peninsula. Although he was entertained in a fine plantation house, he wrote of the country around St. Augustine: "All that is not mud, mud, mud is sand, sand, sand . . . and alligators, snakes, and scorpions."

But from the deck of the *Marion* he gazed with "delightful feelings" on the translucent changeful colors of the water around him, and on the islands with their towering mahoganies and palms, and particularly on the "flocks of birds that covered the shelly beaches," just as Checkerback and his companions covered the beaches this sunny, windy April day a century and a half later.

Near Indian Key, Audubon discovered a bird that had never before been described by science, the great white heron, which he named *Ardea occidentalis,* the heron of the west.

A great white heron was feeding in the shallows now, not far from where Checkerback poked and probed for the eggs of the horseshoe crab. The heron, more than four feet in height and the largest white heron in the world, stood alone and like an alabaster carving at the edge of a sand bar, waiting to spear a shrimp or killifish. The sand bar curved, and then ended not far from some rotted pilings where once there had been a wharf. That wharf had brought a strange kind of fortune to Indian Key.

In Audubon's time the island had been an elegant place. It was even to be made the seat of a new county named for Major Francis Langhorn Dade, a young West Point graduate killed in 1835 in a Christmas ambush by Chief Alligator's forces in the bloody Seminole Wars. The seat of Dade county is now Miami, but in those days Indian Key was the center of a swarming beehive of activity. It was ruled like a tight little kingdom by a New Yorker named Jacob Housman.

On the tiny wind-swept island, dense with mangrove and prickly saw palmetto, Housman built houses, shops, brick cisterns, and even, in a cleared palm-bordered courtyard, a structure he called "The Tropical Hotel." The hotel had a bowling alley, a billiard room, and a taproom. But not many guests came voluntarily to this wilderness resort.

For Housman was a licensed wrecker; he boarded ships in distress and "rescued" whatever he found inside them. In his hotel he accommodated the crew and passengers of the vessels that ran aground on nearby unlighted Carysfort and Alligator reefs, while in the shops he temporarily stored the cargoes. During the years of Housman's control he salvaged a tremendous amount of valuable goods, from pearls to pianos, and he used the profits from the sale of them to enhance his island.

It was an almost perfect situation, and all quite legal. He made only one mistake. Greedy for more money, he sent a message to Washington offering to kill every Indian in his county for two hundred dollars apiece. The message fell into Indian hands.

As it turned out, the man the Indians killed in revenge for this was not Housman at all, but a peaceful botanist living on the island at the time and engaged in nothing more controversial than setting

out the sisal plants that he had brought from Mexico. On that steamy August night in 1840 Housman, already warned of the impending attack, escaped on his wrecking boat. He did not invite Dr. Henry Perrine, the botanist, to go with him. Perrine was scalped, and the entire island was burned.

Housman did not attempt to rebuild his postage-stamp kingdom. Ironically he drowned a year later attempting to board a wreck in a storm. And the weeds and the birds took over Indian Key. Housman's wife set up a marble monument to his memory, but vandals coming to the deserted island chipped it almost completely away. And a hard time they had of it, for it was nearly totally obscured by Dr. Perrine's sharp-leaved sisal plants.

South of Miami, on the road to the Keys, is a village called Perrine. There is no town named Housman. Only a few crumbled and vine-covered cisterns and some rotted pilings indicate that Indian Key was once a flourishing settlement.

Checkerback was filled with an urgency to be on his way. He had a long way still to go; turnstones breed and nest in what is called the High Arctic, as close to the North Pole as any birds will nest. Summer there is a brief time, and the mating and nesting and rearing of young must be accomplished before the long Arctic winter begins, when we who live in the temperate zone still enjoy

early autumn. Migration in spring is accomplished more quickly than the return journey in the fall. At the beginning of the year, the urge to fulfill the breeding cycle pushes the birds on faster. Checkerback's flock rose with a slant of wings and stocky little bodies, and headed on up the Keys.

At one time some of the Keys had been joined together, not simply by bridges and a highway but as peaks in a mountain chain. There are geologists who maintain that the peaks once formed a land bridge between Florida and the Yucatán peninsula of Mexico. And where the peaks were submerged, they still rose so close to the surface that corals found enough sunlight to grow in.

All of this, of course, happened eons ago as counted in geological time. When the polar icecap was formed in a new period of glaciation, the falling sea exposed the corals to air and they died. Rain filtered through their skeletons and through the shells of mollusks also exposed and left stranded by the lowering water. The rain dissolved the limestone from the shells and skeletons, and washed it into the sea, where the waves shaped and reshaped it, washing and pounding until all the fragments became welded into solid rock. The Upper Keys, which follow the existing curve of the mainland, are composed of this limestone. They are actually a fossil coral reef.

The Lower Keys are quite different. Running on a different axis, 42

they are believed to have been all one island in the beginning, emerging from the sea and dividing at the time when the Upper Keys were still a submarine reef of living corals. The limestone of the Lower Keys contained tiny spheres of calcium carbonate which looked so much like fish eggs that the rock was called oölitic, or egglike. Centuries of rain and spray have pitted the surface; there are places on the shore that look and feel like huge hard bathtub sponges.

Sometimes the Lower Keys are called the Pine Islands because of the long-needled Caribbean pines that grow there. One of the Pine Islands, and the largest, is named Big Pine Key. Under the tall straight pines spreads a thick undergrowth of palmetto, scrub oak, and zamia, a plant from which the Indians living in villages on the Key made their arrowroot flour. The same Indians used the poisonous Jamaica dogwood that they found there to catch fish. They called it the "fish-poison tree" and, like the Martiniquais, claimed that when its branches were laid on the water the fish would rise and float on the surface.

The most unusual resident of Big Pine Key is the tiny Key deer, weighing about fifty pounds and standing little more than two feet high. The Spaniards called it the "toy deer." It lives nowhere else in the world, and once was nearly extinct, just as any animal with a limited habitat is in danger of extinction.

Now, however, a refuge has been made for the Key deer on several of the remote Pine Islands, one named "Raccoon," one named "Crane," and one named "No Name." Protected by law from hunting by gun, brush fire, or dog, the toy deer browse unmolested on mangrove leaves and palm seeds, and are gradually increasing in numbers.

Checkerback had never seen a Key deer. The shy little animals did not venture to the crowded beaches where the shorebirds flocked.

Now the turnstones were ready to go again. They rose and wheeled like a single spirit. A pair of willets rose with them, whistling their shrill *pill-willet, pill-will-willet.* Black-bellied plovers, coming rapidly into their full breeding plumage, stood for a moment on the emptying shoal at Big Pine Key, looking out at the clear aquamarine water, the smoky plumes where a sand shark stirred up the marl, the tannin-stained water under the mangrove roots. Then, with their far-carrying cry, they too were on their way.

On the Sea Island

THE WIND, moving in on Georgia from the sea, swung the gray curtains of Spanish moss that looped down from the branches of the live oaks. Like the old saying about the Holy Roman Empire, Spanish moss is neither Spanish nor a moss. It is an air plant, or epiphyte, a member of the pineapple family, botanically known as *Tillandsia*. A story is told that Linnaeus, the great namer of plants, called *Tillandsia* for a student of his, one Elias Tillands, who had such an aversion to water that he once walked a thousand miles around the Gulf of Bothnia rather than cross it.

The story is misleading. Spanish moss does not shun water. In a rainstorm it will turn green and fresh-looking, and insects and other small animals sheltering there will obtain moisture from the sodden strands.

Tillandsia does not kill the tree it grows upon; the relationship is symbiotic rather than parasitic. A parasite will destroy its host plant or animal. Symbiosis means that two organisms can live successfully side by side without damage to one another. The greatest harm that Spanish moss seems to do is to break old branches when it is heavy with rain and whipped by wind.

The wind, this April morning, ruffled the water and laid a net of foam over the combers and a lacy pattern of salt spray on the shelly beach of St. Simons, one of Georgia's sea islands. Checkerback, flying in from the open ocean, landed on a rope of sea wrack,

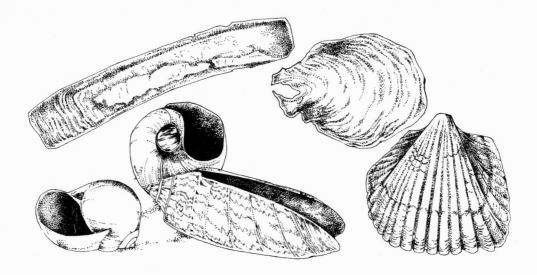

scattering a small cloud of beach fleas. Empty shells lay in every direction. Hungrier than he had ever been before, the ruddy turnstone began pecking at them.

Every empty shell that is swept by waves and tide onto the shingle once held a living animal. These animals, or mollusks, build the calcareous shell in which they live and which protects their soft bodies. They build the shells with an outer fold of their flesh called a mantle which exudes a mixture of lime and hornlike substances. Shells may be smooth or rough, flat or sharply pointed, brightly colored or plain, but they are all fashioned in more or less the same manner, by the creature inside building its house.

Men have always been fascinated by shells, perhaps because of their convolutions, whorls, and spirals, perhaps because of their great variety, perhaps because of the very way that they were constructed. They have been symbols of birth to the Greeks who portrayed their goddess of love, Aphrodite, emerging from the sea in a scallop shell. And an ocean away, the Aztec Indians who had never heard of the Greeks carved on their temples images of their beneficent plumed-serpent god, Quetzalcoatl, borne on a bivalve.

The shells that Checkerback turned over in his anxious search for food lay in deep drifts where the tide had left them. There

46

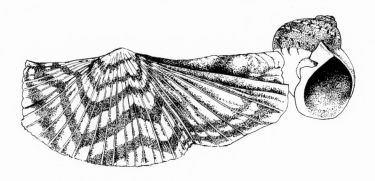

were delicate white angel wings; mossy ponderous arks; shiny olive shells; cowries that are to this day still used as money in some tropical islands; multicolored butterfly-like coquinas; razor clams; iridescent jingle shells; and the smooth eye-patterned case of the moon snail.

It is ironic that the moon snail has an eye design on its shell, because the moon snail is blind. It has to feel its way under the sand to find food. When it lays its eggs on the beach it leaves a raised rim of sand, called a "collar," to protect them. Checkerback shuffled through a collar and left it in fragments.

The house that the moon snail builds is also a favorite dwelling place of the hermit crab. With no hard covering of their own, hermit crabs depend on the empty shells they find to protect their soft bodies. As they grow and need larger shells they trade one for another, slithering quickly out of one into the next. Often two or more hermits will fight over an abandoned shell, pulling it this way and that. This battle sometimes becomes so fierce that the combatants will forget the shell. Then a third hermit, scurrying by, is apt to make off with the prize.

The wind was increasing. More shorebirds arrived and they huddled together, pointing into the flying foam. They were tired, and torn between their two needs—to rest and feed—and to be

47

on their way. Plovers and curlews, sandpipers and yellowlegs rested with the turnstones on their northward journey, and heard the whistling of the wind through the moss-draped oaks—the live oaks, the water oaks, the laurel oaks of St. Simons.

Oaks have always been one of the most revered and impressive of trees. Live oaks, with their vast spreading canopies and their glossy evergreen foliage, have massive trunks and low-bending branches that dip almost to the ground. Sometimes these branches bear a whole forest of resurrection fern, a polypody so named because after a rainstorm its apparently dead brown fronds rise up fresh and verdant. In the spring the old leaves fall with a sound like a gentle shower, and on the sea-island plantations there is the sound of raking.

In Georgia they say that a live oak takes a hundred years to grow, lives for another hundred, and finally takes a hundred more to die. Then the wood was prized for shipbuilding in the days of the great sailing ships; the ribs of the frigate *Old Ironsides* were made from sea-island live oak.

The Druids, who revered oak trees, would surely have been inspired by a live oak if they had ever seen one. Tree worship is one of the earliest forms of pagan religion. Pointing toward heaven, trees must have seemed rather like signals, just as birds, arriving from the sky, were thought to be messengers of the gods.   48

Indeed history is full of accounts of signal trees that directed armies, and of Indians who tied up tree branches to mark new trails, as did the cattlemen when they drove their herds to new pastures. Charter and treaty oaks and elms are named for the historic documents signed in their shade.

In some forms of tree worship, the god was actually believed to inhabit the tree. Many deities had their particular sacred trees. The oak was holy to no less than Jupiter, king of the gods, and also to Hercules, their doorkeeper.

Today Christians all around the world bring evergreens into their houses at Christmastime. Perhaps many of them would be surprised and even shocked to learn that this is an ancient pagan custom. Before the winter solstice, close to the date significantly chosen to celebrate the birth of Christ, the hours of daylight have become shorter and shorter, and the days darker and darker. Primitive people feared that the days might become so short that eventually there would be no light at all. Therefore they brought into their houses (or caves or castles) evergreen boughs that were to them the symbols of life, apparently unchanging and enduring. And when they noticed that the days were indeed growing gradually longer again, they supposed that the greens had protected them from eternal darkness. Every year thereafter, as the hours of light grew short, these early inhabitants of the world brought in their

evergreens, and sure enough, every year at the same time the days began to lengthen.

We still touch wood to propitiate a tree-god. Celts in Europe worshiped their sky-god in the form of an oak. And Druids revered their oaks beyond all other trees and taught that the round evergreen clumps of mistletoe growing on them were endowed with mysterious powers. It was an old Celtic tradition that mistletoe had flourished as a tree until it was called upon to furnish the wood for Christ's cross. From then on it was condemned to live as a parasite. Even today some churches, which allow the holly and ivy as traditional Christmas decorations, still ban the mistletoe.

The word "druid" is believed to come from the old Welsh *derwydd,* or "oak seer," one who gleaned both knowledge and inspiration from oaks, and later conveyed this wisdom in ceremonial and occult poetic mysteries. Caesar mentions Druids in Gaul going to Britain for training in their secret rites, adding that they taught of "the stars and their motions, the world, the size of lands, natural philosophy, and the nature of the gods."

Once a year the Druids cut down the mistletoe from their oaks with a golden sickle, gold being sacred to the sun, a supreme deity. A dryad, or wood nymph, was their oak fairy. Our very word "door" comes from the Druid word *der* and the Sanskrit *dwr,* both meaning oak. The tree was considered so strong that its name was 50

given to that barrier which protected the inhabitants of a dwelling from a foe, or from a stranger, or the weather.

Closer to Checkerback's beach than the moss-festooned live oaks, a few palmettos, the cabbage and the saw, bent in the wind. Their pointed fronds contrasted sharply with the smooth shapes of oak and moss, lending variety and accent to the landscape. Palms too have an ancient history.

The Tree of Life in the Babylonian version of the Garden of Eden legend was a palm. The date palm, sacred to the Egyptian goddess of the trinity, Isis, mother of the sun-god, gave its scientific name, *phoenix,* to the fabled bird of the sun-worshiping Egyptian priests.

Pliny the Elder described the phoenix as being the size of an eagle, with a purple body, azure tail, and golden neck. It lived in a desert paradise, to the east of Egypt where the sun rose. Every five hundred years—or a thousand, some legends say—it gathered aromatic spices and built a nest of them in a tall date palm. Sparks from the hoofs of horses pulling the sun-god's chariot across the sky set fire to the phoenix nest and the bird died. But from the ashes it was reborn and rose again fresh and young. The phoenix is still used in many lands as a symbol of immortality and resurrection. And Phoenicia, the ancient country with which the palm shares its name, once spread out across the whole eastern Mediterranean Sea.

Between the live oaks and palmettos and the windy beach of St. Simons stood the remains of Fort Frederica. In 1773, James E. Oglethorpe, former member of Parliament and a general who had fought in Turkey, arranged for the founding of the last of the thirteen original colonies. On what was then the border between "Carolina" and "the Florida Territory," General Oglethorpe drew out boundaries, settled Savannah, and became the first governor of Georgia.

A few years later England ran into trouble with Spain, and "The War of Jenkins's Ear" was begun. It was called by that odd name because a Spanish revenue officer had cut off an ear of a British smuggler named Jenkins, and this was supposed to have been one of the factors that precipitated the conflict.

Early in the war, Oglethorpe, with a small fleet and some men from his own Highland Regiment, tried unsuccessfully to capture the Spanish-held fort at St. Augustine. It was a valiant attempt, but the well-designed fort and its defenders stood firm.

Then the Spanish retaliated. Thirty ships sailed from Havana Harbor, anchored at St. Augustine to pick up more troops, and then sailed on to St. Simons Island where they had little difficulty

capturing Fort Frederica. But they had not reckoned on the courage and cunning of the British general. Oglethorpe rounded up as many Creek Indians as he could find, and with them lay in wait for the Spaniards advancing beyond the fort. The place of ambush is descriptively known as the Bloody Marsh, and it was as far as the Spaniards ever got.

Checkerback walked along the thick, crumbling, salt-bleached walls of the fortification, as much at home as on a breakwater. Gulls had opened mussel and oyster shells there; sometimes a scrap of food remained, or a beetle seeking cover in the convolutions of a whelk. In a desultory fashion, Checkerback turned over what few shells he found, and then stood looking out at the scene below.

The wind was dying; more and more shorebirds, tired from being buffeted by it, dropped down into the sheltering marsh grasses and onto the gleaming mud flats, misted over with spume. On the wind-etched beach, where blown-off ropes of Spanish moss still harbored insects, the birds poked among the strands, or posed, facing the dying wind, like little wooden figures on the sand.

Beaches are sometimes called the battlegrounds of the earth. But the wars are not between the Spanish and the English, or the Calusa and the Carib. The opponents are the sea and the land, and in spite

of the peaceful appearance of most beaches, the wars waged there are more violent and long-lasting than any waged by human armies.

The battle has been going on for unimaginable numbers of years. Even more unimaginable is that the battle will end. Wind seems to be the chief protagonist.

In from the sea, wave by wave, water pours up on the shore, and drags on back. With it each receding wave carries sand and silt, fragments of shell and fishbone and the carapace of crustaceans, all of the debris of the beach, most of which it had originally placed there. When it returns again it makes a similar deposit. It is the wind that has set the waves in motion.

Out from the land blow sand and silt, grasses, leaves, and seed pods, moved by the onshore wind. Rain scuds; banks and dunes are eroded. Tides rise and fall, bringing in and carrying away. The contour of the shore is in a constant state of flux. The sea, by contrast, over countless centuries gives no outward appearance of having changed at all.

Sand beaches, like the one where shorebirds now gathered in hordes and over which the ruddy turnstone stared out from General Oglethorpe's fortification, are the product of millions of years of this conflict. They began with the pounding and grinding of the sea upon the shore, whether that shore was coral, rock, or lava. Every grain of sand has its origins in geological time.

54

Wind and rain, as well as the waves, move the grains of sand along, transferring one here and another there in the endless flux of erosion and construction. Over the period of one summertime a beach will not appear to change very much, unless a hurricane or "August blow" carves out deep runnels or builds new dunes. But over a period of fifty years, or sometimes much less, a beach may become almost unrecognizable, so altered may it be. Sand, taken from one shore, can be laid down on another, hundreds of miles away.

The sand on Checkerback's Georgia beach was mostly pale quartz, but there were other mineral granules that streaked the surface, giving it in places a marbleized quality. Pinpoints of mica glistened here and there among the dark streakings; when the sun shone through the drifting clouds the beach sparkled like crystal. Bits of animal-built calcium, ground and reground against coral reef and rock, also contributed to the variety of that strip of land between earth and ocean where the living descendants of the same animals eked out a tenuous and precarious existence.

What could be more difficult than living in the intertidal zone of any beach? There, for half of its daily life, the animal is, or may be, submerged in surging water, and for the other half left stranded in quite a different medium, the unstable sand, open to sun and wind and predator.

55

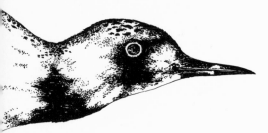

An animal, confronted with an unknown and therefore possibly hostile environment, has three choices that it can make. It may move on to what might be a less hostile environment; it may, over uncountable years, make physiological adaptations to enable it to adjust to its new habitat; or it may perish.

The ancestors of the multitudinous dwellers of the narrow strip between land and sea, faced with these decisions, obviously chose to adapt. It is true that some of them did move away and try a new existence. It is equally true that many more perished. But in those early days when animals first emerged from their salubrious and familiar wet habitat and set foot on dry, or drying, earth, some must have decided, or been forced, to remain right there where they arrived. Others were driven to the beach by fierce competition farther inland. They are the ancestors of the moon snail, the starfish, the sand dollar, and the razor clam.

If the beach is a difficult environment for animals to live in, it is equally hard for plants. They too, and before the animals—for there have always been plants before animals—have been forced to move, to adapt, or to perish. In their seaside habitat, they also have to cope with shifting sands, blazing sun where there is little or no shade, and buffeting wind where there is little or no protection. Then, too, they must endure burning salt spray. It is the same

salt spray that, when hurricane winds whip the leaves from the mangroves and other coastal trees, is blown onto the trunks and branches, making the shore look as though a fire had raced through.

Beach plants survive in their hazardous habitat by adaptively developing tough stems and leaves that withstand the battering elements and store water against drought, much the way that the cacti and other vegetation of the deserts of the southwest have done. On the shifting shore of St. Simons, the plants just above the high-tide line are mostly succulents, water-storing and salt-tolerant. Further back, waving sea oats, pointed Spanish bayonet, wax myrtle, and yaupon, or sea-island holly, had managed to survive the constant assault of the sea wind.

Without these plants the beach animals would find their environment even more treacherous. Shore vegetation provides shade from the summer sun and shelter from the winter gales. Its roots hold down the dunes and help to keep the sand on the ever-changing beach from washing and blowing away.

Checkerback flew into a patch of sea oats where another turnstone was feeding. This bird was a year older; he had already made several round trips from the tundra to the jungle and back. Now he was on his way again to his Arctic summerland.

The older turnstone had found a dozen or more sand fleas in

a wreath of drenched *Tillandsia* that the wind had blown from the branch of a live oak. When it saw Checkerback approaching, it took a few steps forward, raised its wings aggressively, and let out a warning squawk. It was not willing to lose one sand flea to another bird. Checkerback, who had not known about the fleas, backed off in surprise. Then, recovering his poise, he started at once to dig little holes in the sand with his stout bill, even though he found nothing whatever in the bottom of the holes.

Arenaria interpres was scientifically described for the first time from just such a shelly beach in Georgia as the one where Checkerback now foraged. Linnaeus, in his *Systema Naturae,* based his description largely on "The Turn-Stone," written by Mark Catesby as part of his two large folios, *The Natural History of Carolina, Florida, and the Bahama Islands,* vividly illustrated by the author, and published in London in several sections between 1731 and 1743. In those days when Catesby was observing the ruddy turnstone, Georgia had not yet even been named a colony by General Oglethorpe.

Mark Catesby was born in England in 1679. He was related to Robert Catesby who, along with Guy Fawkes, conceived the idea of the famous Gunpowder Plot. Young Mark, already an artist and ornithologist, had a longing to find and paint the birds of the New World. When he was thirty he made his first trip to North America,   58

and he stayed for seven years. Three years later, in 1722, he was
back, and he stayed for four years more. During this time he painted
a notable number of birds, and wrote with more naïveté than
modesty: "I believe very few Birds have escaped my Knowledge,
excepting some Water Fowl and some of those which frequent the
Sea."

Catesby's art anticipated and perhaps inspired Audubon's in its
depicting of birds—often stylized although at the same time posed
in animated attitudes—on blossoming branches or decorative garlands. Actually he was also a botanist by profession, as his paintings
attest.

And he was most of all an excellent observer. He was one of
the first bird watchers to declare that contrary to popular belief
swallows did not bury themselves in the muddy bottoms of ponds
to hibernate through the cold winter months. People had seen
swallows in migration, skimming low over the water to catch
insects and drink. The next day they were gone, and so the rumor
started that they had plunged underwater to wait in the mud for
spring. Mark Catesby knew better.

John Bartram, Lord Baltimore, Benjamin Franklin, William Byrd,
and John Randolph were all interested in Catesby's American work.
Incidentally, the word "American" came into common usage during
the War of Jenkins's Ear. Up to that time, English-speaking residents of this new country had been called "Colonials."

A flock of half a dozen ruddy turnstones landed not two yards from where Checkerback was still probing the sand. Remembering his rebuff from the older turnstone, Checkerback kept his distance.

But the little flock was not aggressive. The birds seemed to be exhausted. Huddled together on the beach, they did not forage for food, but stood almost motionless near a wrack of Sargasso weed and the shiny abandoned shell of a horseshoe crab. Each one pointed in the direction from which it had come, and from which the wind had so recently poured in.

Checkerback ambled over and made himself one with the waiting group. All in similar plumage, it was impossible to distinguish one male from another. No bird made a sound.

Only a pair of black-necked stilts, bending their long legs to feed, let out a series of shrill whistles at a solitary willet which had ventured too close. Tree frogs were calling from the mossy oaks, and inland in the pine and holly forest a wild turkey gobbled.

The two turnstone flocks merged and became one. On a sudden impulse they rose and whirled away in a cloudlike formation, now separating, now coming together again, dipping and twisting, their neat bodies shining in the gold light that came from the low sun through the Spanish moss. A few more turns and whirls, and they had left the sea island behind.

Carolina

THE FIRST BIRD that we know anything about was called *Archae-opteryx,* or "Ancient wing." One hundred and forty million years ago it glided from the branch of a tree and sailed out over a Bavarian lake.

How can we assume this? There were no bird watchers in the Mesozoic era because there were no birds. We may imagine that whatever animals roamed the earth at that time stared with some wonder at this feathered flying reptile.

"Ancient wing" did not make a very long journey; its attempted flight was a short one; it fell into the lake. Only millions of years later could it be said to have achieved success. Workmen, cutting slate in the dried lake bottom in 1861, came across a fossil impression left by the bird when tons of water pressed down on its body in the sediment and silt.

The fossil found in that limestone quarry showed that *Archae-opteryx lithographica* was indeed feathered, and of all our vast array of animals through the ages, only birds have had feathers. The fossil also showed definite reptilian traits: claws on the wings, a bony tail, and the heavy bones that may have prevented its flight across the lake. Were it not for its feathers it would probably have been classed as a reptile. As it is, it has been called the "missing link" between birds and reptiles.

The crow-sized *Archaeopteryx* had claws on the elbow, or bend,

of its wing for the purpose of climbing trees. Today we could not imagine a bird with claws on its wings, and yet in the steaming mangrove swamps of the Amazon, not far from the beach where Checkerback spent his winters, there is such a bird. The young hoatzin, called *cigaña,* or "gypsy" in Brazil, is hatched with claws on its wings which it uses to grasp branches as it makes its way through the jungle. In mature birds the claws disappear, but the fact remains that here seems to be a kind of living "Ancient wing."

The *Archaeopteryx* that drowned in the water was a land bird. Water fowl and shorebirds evolved much later.

How difficult it is for us to imagine a world without birds! Yet we know there was such a time. What made the reptiles take to the air in the first place? We can only conclude that it was for much the same reason that mangroves left the dry land to become water trees, and orchids left the ground to become air plants—that is, competition and overcrowding. Giant dinosaurs were taking over the land; smaller reptiles were being driven either underground or up into trees. From the trees they eventually began to fly as *ptero-saurs,* or "winged lizards."

But the first true bird, over countless centuries of evolution, had developed adaptations for its aboreal life. It had long slender feet for perching on branches, lighter teeth for eating more delicate and often airborne food, and the beginnings of warm-bloodedness, which, of all the animals, only birds and mammals have ever had.

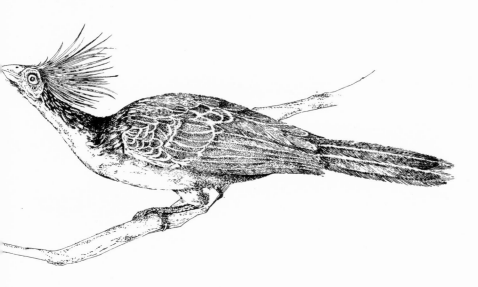

We call "Ancient wing" the original bird. This does not mean that there were not other and older reptilian feathered birds. Perhaps the *Archaeopteryx* evolved over millions of years of adaptations. We only know that the first feathered flying animal on record left its frail skeleton in the Jurassic mud, and that from then on all birds have been called its descendants.

Checkerback might have been surprised to be called a descendant of "Ancient wing." He did not resemble the fossil in the slightest. There was nothing lizardlike or tenuously reptilian in his chunky, compact little body; he could fly over numberless lakes and far wider stretches of water without danger of falling in. And no animals looked up amazed to see him passing overhead.

The turnstone, on the other hand, surveyed the fort below him with a feeling almost of recognition. It was one of several that he had encountered since leaving Brazil. The flock of shorebirds with which he was traveling wheeled at the sight of it, and dropped down on the parade ground. Checkerback thus had a chance for his first glimpse of Charleston Harbor. It had been night when he had passed over Fort Sumter the other times.

He was on a tiny island. Behind him, as he faced the city, lay the Atlantic Ocean over which he had flown to South Carolina. Before him pointed the apex where two rivers met, the Battery. Behind that was Charleston, the dreaming, historic city of tall spires and leafy, walled gardens.

What happened at Fort Sumter in 1861, the same year the *Archaeopteryx* was found, was both simple and significant. An old man fired a shot. This occurred on April 12 and it marked the beginning of the Civil War.

Brigadier General Pierre Gustave Toutant Beauregard, newly appointed to the Confederate Army, had been called upon to protect Charleston Harbor from possible northern attack. As in the case of Key West, the town's island fortress was in federal hands. Major Robert Anderson was in charge, with Captain Abner Doubleday, far better known as the "Father of Baseball," second in command.

"Do not desire needlessly to bombard Fort Sumter," urged Jefferson Davis, President of the Confederacy, in a telegram to Beauregard. Major Anderson is reported to have said to his adversaries: "If we never meet in this world again, God grant that we may meet in the next." Then he told his own soldiers that a battle was about to begin.

At four-thirty in the morning the first shot was fired, through sentiment and prearrangement, by one Edmund Ruffin, a planter and dedicated leader of the secessionist movement. His white hair in a short pigtail, he had slept all night in his uniform so as to be sure not to miss this signal honor. The fire from his shot glowed in the air "like the wings of a firefly," and exploded over Fort Sumter. Shortly afterwards the Confederacy held complete control of Charleston Harbor.

The migrating birds, having rested, were busily searching for food along the ramparts of the fort. The April sun, reflected from the walls, baked down on them. Checkerback was torn by his impatience to be on his way and his need to remain with his flock, the companions with which he had traveled so far. He had not mated the summer before; he had been too young. He had not even reached the High Arctic where his parents had mated and where he had been hatched. Now he felt stirrings of restlessness and anxiety. Tentatively he flew a short distance to a mud flat where hundreds of shorebirds had congregated. He looked back but none of his flock had followed. Checkerback lost himself in a vast congregation of plovers, sandpipers, willets, yellowlegs, and knots.

While not precisely water birds in the same sense as the pelagic ocean-voyaging shearwaters and gannets, or the water fowl classification of ducks and geese, shorebirds are generally thought of as more water birds than land birds. On that marginal, narrow band where earth and water meet are crowded from time to time more birds at once than are found anywhere else. Water birds seem to find coastlines, including the offshore islands, if not ideal at least satisfactory for feeding and resting, mating and egg laying. In tremendous colonies they carry out their vital processes, and they are certainly the most abundant birds in the world.

The "bird islands" of the northern coast of Scotland are famous for their gannet, puffin, murre, and kittiwake colonies. In the Shet-

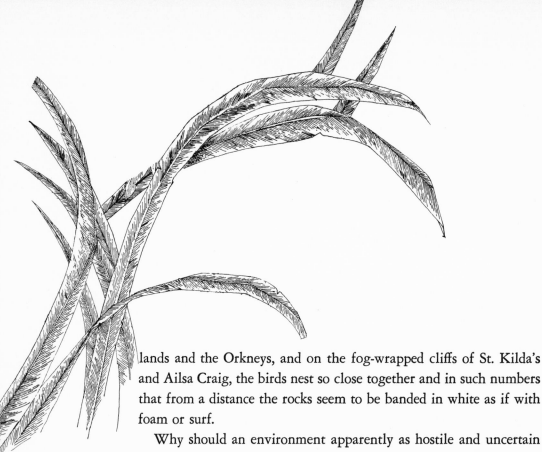

lands and the Orkneys, and on the fog-wrapped cliffs of St. Kilda's and Ailsa Craig, the birds nest so close together and in such numbers that from a distance the rocks seem to be banded in white as if with foam or surf.

Why should an environment apparently as hostile and uncertain as the open sea encourage such vast hordes of wildlife? Principally it seems to be a matter of that primary requirement—food. The ocean, with its apparently never-ending source of fish and plankton, its protein and minerals, particularly nitrogen, provides a ceaseless supply of nourishing meals for the birds, which, because of their high body metabolism and rapid digestion, must feed for a large part of their waking time. A dry environment could not possibly supply such avian hordes with adequate sustenance. The ocean, with its great depth, provides, one might say, the extra needed dimension.

Then too, the longer winter nights of northern regions so dimly illuminate the waters that vegetation, which requires sunlight, cannot survive in the murky deep. Therefore it floats up toward the surface. And after it follow the fish and crustaceans that feed on it. They in turn provide food for the throngs of water birds.

Checkerback continued his feeding on the mud flat not far from Charleston Harbor. Behind the mud flats and salt marshes began. Salt marshes are relatively open stretches of bare or grassy land

which are periodically flooded by the tide. Sand and mud, and sometimes marl and lime, combine to produce a soil that is acceptable to salt-tolerant, or halophytic, vegetation. *Spartina,* the cord grass, and *salicornia,* the saltwort, along with other succulents and rushes and sedges, manage to survive in this saline habitat.

Because of its very salinity, or saltiness, only a few highly specialized plants can flourish in such an environment. And even these few have difficulty getting started. As on a beach, unbroken winds and tides come and go and change the landscape. Storm tides sweep through; spring and fall tides produce flooding. The salt content of the soil alters after heavy rains. All of these variations add to the precariousness of life for salt-marsh plants.

Salt-marsh animals also have a precarious time. Sometimes they are carried in from the open sea to this totally strange environment by a storm wave, and left stranded there when the wave recedes. Small fish and crustaceans, swept into the marsh, dry out and die and become food for patrolling gulls. Some of the sea animals are able to burrow beneath the surface, and, finding their required moisture, wait for another wave. Many snails climb grasses to escape the rising waters. And most of the salt-marsh animals are eagerly hunted by both resident and migrating birds.

67   On this spring morning the South Carolina salt marsh was flooded,

not by a high tide, but by a tremendous flock of red-winged black-birds. They dropped down onto the grasses like one of the nets thrown by a Martinique fisherman, rising and falling again, and utter-ing a fantastic variety of sounds. The air rang with their clamor. Checkerback heard it as he fed.

Boat-tailed grackles strutted along the mud runnels, looking for snails. So did some black-necked stilts. They flew belligerently at the grackles, then skittered away and dropped down again, their long legs dangling. Little blue, and Louisiana, herons stalked slowly by, stirring up the water with one foot, and peering down for a frog to spear.

Long-billed marsh wrens were beginning to nest in the tall grasses, chattering as they searched for dried bits of spartina to carry in their curved bills. Wary, chickenlike rails scurried among the rushes along the creek banks, and then froze and probed the mud, hunting for crabs. The marsh was alive with insects enjoying the new warmth; their humming was like that of one great beehive.

Not far from the salt marsh stood what was left of an ancient cy-press swamp. All swamps have ancient origins. We understand that life itself began in the swampy waters of the oldest known rivers: the Nile, the Tigris, and the Euphrates. Trees then, we have learned from studying the same kind of fossils that told the story of "Ancient wing," were not the same as our trees today. Ferns and club mosses,

the groundcovers of our present woods, once formed the canopies of antique forests, shading dinosaurs and sheltering the *Archaeopteryx.*

Cypresses are almost as old as the swamps they live in. Like the oaks of the Druids, cypress trees have their worshipers too. They appeared in the holy pictures of early Crete; they were sacred to the goddess Artemis, or Diana, the huntress. And like the phoenix, the cypress has also been considered a resurrection symbol, and is often planted in churchyards.

Mangroves are known in many parts of the world simply as water trees. Cypresses are too. Over centuries of evolution they adapted characteristics that enabled them to survive in the wetlands where most trees cannot grow at all.

Since roots cannot secure themselves firmly in swampy soil, cypresses developed "buttresses" to keep their massive trunks upright, supporting their broad crowns. And since available oxygen is scarce in waterlogged soil, cypresses are believed to have fashioned for themselves air-breathing "knees," conical projections which, like the mangroves' pneumatophores, apparently enable them to endure.

Like all life, plants began in water. Eventually a few—the liverworts were the first—attempted the leap to a strange and hostile habitat. Long slow adaptations turned the hostile habitat into a beneficial home. In fact the plants flourished so successfully that

some were driven back to the old watery existence. Evolution, as it turns out, is full of circles and ironies.

There was a time when the Carolina Santee cypress swamp was alive and noisy with one of the most colorful and attractive birds this country has ever seen. Mark Catesby, in his extensive ornithological excursions through the Southeast, first described the bird, as he did the ruddy turnstone in Georgia, and he called it "The Parrot of Carolina."

That was in 1731. In 1664, in London, a New World traveler named William Hilton published his journals which contained an account of the "great flocks of Parrakeeto's" he had observed along the coast of the Province of Carolina. John and William Bartram, the Philadelphia Quaker father and son whom we call our first ecologists, were studying birds and plants in Carolina in 1765 when they watched sociable, readily approachable flocks of the raucous and gaudy birds "hovering and fluttering on their cypress tops." The birds were Carolina paroquets.

Today one could walk for miles and miles through the cypress stands of the South and not hear one squawk nor catch a single glimpse of the apple-green and golden-yellow birds circling and flashing through the trees. The only parrot of temperate North America is believed to have joined that spectral company of extinct animals.

Why did it disappear? One reason is that brightly colored plumage is a hazard to birds. Their very beauty endangers them; they are martyrs to their own splendor. Roseate spoonbills were shot in the Everglades to have their crimson-splashed wings made into ladies' fans. The Central American quetzal of the high rain forests was killed for its plumage; Aztec featherworkers wove its plumes into robes and headdresses for Montezuma and his high priests. But the paroquet was shot for other reasons too. Farmers, naturally enough, resented its destructive raids on their fruit crops and cornfields.

It is impossible to state with any kind of accuracy when the last Carolina paroquet was seen. Unlike the last passenger pigeon which died on a specific date in a specific cage, stray parrots are still reported from time to time. Usually the reports turn out to be of escaped pet birds, or stowaways from West Indian banana boats.

The cypress swamp of the Santee was once the home of another spectacular bird, now also vanished. The indefatigable Mark Catesby introduced it to science for the first time as "the largest white-bill Wood-pecker" in his *Natural History of Carolina.* No ivory-billed woodpecker has been recorded from the Santee since the late 1930s.

The loss of anything irreplaceable is bound to be tragic. Evolution does not repeat itself. The long cycle of adaptations from the *Archaeopteryx* to the ivorybill cannot be rolled backward, nor can it ever again create a Carolina paroquet, a dodo, a great auk, or a

heath hen. Now even the strict laws enforced for bird protection may not be able to save all the endangered species: the eskimo curlew, the Everglades kite, the California condor, and the whooping crane, of which recently less than fifty remained, are only a few whose futures hang in the balance.

Environments change, forests are cut down for timber; swamps are filled in for developments. With our expanding population, more and more people need places in which to live. A hundred years ago it was not unusual to see scores of passenger pigeons roosting in a tall chestnut tree. Today both the birds and the trees are gone.

The ruddy turnstone, fortunately, is not one of our endangered species. Checkerback, on his journeys, encounters innumerable others of his own kind. And yet no one should dare to make specific statements about the future. Audubon once saw passenger pigeons in flocks so dense that, in his now famous phrase, they "darkened the sky."

There was a time when the Santee was called a "rice river." Rice had been the great productive crop of the Carolina low country; its cultivation and export enabled its growers to build stately ante-bellum mansions on their plantations. Along the broad coastal rivers, crossed and recrossed by ruffling tides, stretched the rice fields, pale green in spring and yellow-gold in fall.

Although very little rice is grown anymore, many of the flooded

fields remain. And they are visited every year by thousands of water fowl on migration.

Thousands of shorebirds were migrating on this warm spring morning. On the barrier beaches facing the ocean they patterned the sand like cloud shadows passing over. Checkerback dropped down on the narrow strip of sand and found the flock of turnstones he had been traveling with. The flock was larger now; other turnstones had joined it. Feeling at home, Checkerback moved in among them.

The wind that had blown so hard at St. Simons barely stirred the sea oats and pennywort on the Carolina dunes. Behind the dunes a fresh-water pond reflected the cobalt sky. Phoebes were calling from the low willows as they snatched insects and then returned to the branch from which they had flown. Yellowthroats peered out curiously at any sound or movement.

Beyond the pond a forest began. Cardinals and Carolina wrens whistled from the tangle of vines—smilax, jessamine, and cat brier—where they were nesting. The vines overran the trunks of live oaks, magnolias, loblolly pines, and the inevitable palmettos. Here and there a dogwood or wild cherry shone like a white veil.

Through a tidal creek where black skimmers, the "cut-waters" of Mark Catesby, were shearing the surface with their black-tipped red mandibles, a fisherman in a raveled straw hat and a pink shirt

that had once been red was poling his skiff. The fisherman was a
boy of twelve or thirteen, and he stopped his poling to watch some
egrets, gleaming as white as china against the pickerelweed, and a
great blue heron spearing frogs. The skiff ran into a clump of reeds
and for a moment held fast, before the current started to swing the
stern around. In that moment, Checkerback, having glimpsed some
fiddler crabs, left-over bait, on the bow, flew onto the skiff and
snatched a crab. Since the afternoon that he had spent probing the
bait buckets on the Overseas Highway to the Keys, under the pelicans' watchful eyes, this was the nearest that he had approached a
human being. The boy stared, frozen in surprise, and knew that he
would have something to tell at supper that evening.

The turnstone, hungry now for more fiddlers, began hunting on
the pitted bank of the flooded inlet. The crabs, though, were quicker
than he was. Holding one claw aloft, like violinists with their instruments, they scuttled across the aerated mud and slid into their
holes. Checkerback had to content himself with feeding on an exposed bed of coon oysters. He had tasted these before, on the arching mangrove roots of the Florida islands. But other turnstones had
found the bed before him; Checkerback's growing hunger was not
quickly satisfied.

His group, larger now than ever, was pointing in the direction of
the north. It would not be long before they were off again.

75

The Outermost Beach

THE RUDDY TURNSTONE, *Arenaria interpres,* stood hunched up in the wind, its feathers ruffled, its left foot engaged in scratching its bill. But Checkerback was not as miserable as he looked. His ruffled feathers were a means of insulating his body against the unaccustomed cold.

Birds have relatively high body temperatures, about 106 degrees Fahrenheit. This is markedly higher than our normal temperature, and, as in all warm-blooded animals, is maintained more or less constantly. When birds sleep at night, their temperature may drop a few degrees. Nocturnal birds, like owls and whippoorwills, have higher temperatures at night.

In any case birds' temperatures are not affected by climate; tropical species are as warm-blooded as those in the High Arctic. Nor are they affected by seasonal changes. A chickadee at a window feeder in a blizzard maintains the same temperature as when it is nesting in the summery pine woods.

The way that feathers insulate the birds' bodies is by stabilizing the air next to the skin and thus preventing the loss of heat. The more the feathers are ruffled, the more heat is preserved. This is most easily accomplished when the birds are standing still. That is why Checkerback's flock, with their heads tucked into their feathers to breathe warmed air, looked like a colony of puffballs.

They were standing on the easternmost sand beach of the con- 76 tinental United States. Where the Cape Cod peninsula reaches out its arm and bends its elbow around Cape Cod Bay, with Nantucket Sound beneath it, the vast unbroken sweep of the Atlantic pounds in from the direction of Spain. Atlantic winds shape and reshape the high concave dunes. On this outermost beach the turnstones huddled, and Checkerboard had his first taste on this journey of what it would be like where he was going.

Birds are better adapted to polar conditions than other animals are, including polar bears and humans. Penguins and Arctic terns endure their frozen communities far better than mammals do, and survive in more frigid climates. Man has lived at the poles, it is true, but with insulated clothing, furs, and fire. With their high rate of metabolism, birds eat more and faster, and the food is rapidly turned into body heat. And then they have their insulating feathers.

Checkerback, hatched in the Arctic Circle and now on his way back again, felt the cold and sensed that his journey was nearing its end. He had come a long way since the April afternoon when he had stood in the sun on the Carolina mud flat and heard the cardinals whistling from the jessamine and seen the blackbirds circling over the flooded rice fields. Actually he still had a long way to go.

He had passed wind-swept Cape Hatteras jutting out into the ocean, with its lighthouses and weather station, its bleached drift-wood fragments, and its skeletons of wrecks. Ribs of many a ship

arched up out of the blowing sand, testifying to the violence of the waves. Tree trunks that once stood in great forests rolled in the surf or lay half-buried by dune, catching shreds of rockweed and providing perching places for gulls, and they too testified to the violence that had eroded the shore and washed away the woodlands.

Cape Hatteras is a familiar name; it is a name associated with storms. One can hardly think of it without thinking of rough weather. In its unique position on the outer banks of North Carolina, jutting straight out into the Atlantic, Hatteras Island sees at least twenty large vessels a day pass by its lightship. And it is said that seven hundred ships with a displacement of over fifty tons each have sunk beneath the surface of the turbulent waters.

One of the most famous of these was the *Monitor,* the federal gunboat which defeated the *Merrimack* in the early part of the Civil War at Hampton Roads, Virginia. The *Monitor* went down while being towed past the Cape by a side-wheeler. The accident occurred only a few months after the gunboat's victory, and the bodies that washed ashore were buried on the spot by Union soldiers and covered with rocks from the first lighthouse, built in 1797.

The beam from the present lighthouse at Hatteras reaches out to sea for twenty miles, and shipwrecks are far fewer than they used to be. But the swiftly moving Gulf Stream, which rolls like a broad river through the Atlantic, surges past Cape Hatteras only twenty-five

miles offshore. And weather, and the conditions that cause it, have never been changed by the building of a lighthouse or the perfecting of a high-powered lens.

Weather has been called the stimulus that sets a bird off on its migration journey. The idea that they leave their wintering grounds because of lack of food cannot be true. In the tropics, or subtropics, there is bound to be more than sufficient available nourishment. On the other hand, a bird must not arrive at his northern nesting ground too soon or he will find it still icebound. If he arrives too late he may not have time for his nesting cycle and rearing of young before the ice once more closes in. It must be, then, the weather that gives the signal and triggers the impulse to be off.

Climate, while usually considered along with weather, is actually something quite different. It is weather studied over a long period of time, and measured in seasons and years, instead of in days and even hours. Weather may change rapidly; climate does not. People in Maryland claim that they have beautiful weather but a terrible climate; people in Massachusetts say they have a beautiful climate but terrible weather. Much of this, of course, is in the point of view.

Climate, which is largely determined by temperature and precipitation, decrees what plants and animals can live in a certain region. Birds, the only warm-blooded animals with the ability to make long

flights, are able for the most part to fly away from unfavorable seasonal changes. Some, however, are not. In the Antarctic, emperor penguins huddle together to keep warm. Snow buntings and Arctic grouse have been known to bury themselves in snowbanks to get out of the bitter wind. Ptarmigans and snowy owls have feathered feet to enable them to walk on the snow, and protective white coloration to help keep them from being pounced on by wolves or Arctic foxes.

Checkerback, in spite of his urgency to reach the tundra, was still a long way from the Arctic. In his large flock, he had whirled away from the windy beach of Hatteras; undulating and flapping and sailing, but straight on course, he made his way up the Atlantic coast. Before him lay the peninsula to which three states had given their name: Delmarva.

The ruddy turnstone found himself in the flat and grassy tide-water country surrounding the Chesapeake Bay. Wide, wet meadows where geese and ducks had fed, and rails sought shelter, stretched out on every side. The wild swans, which most of the winter had rimmed the edges of the bay with a band of white like surf breaking on rocks, had already gone. In lookout trees, of cedar or sweet gum, ospreys had built their bulky, bushel-basket nests and sat peering out watchfully, or soared with high-pitched screams and dived for fish. Oaks and sycamores lined the distances as far as the eye   80

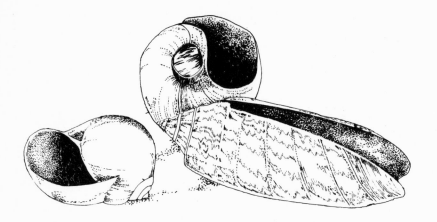

could see. The palm and mangrove had long since been left behind.

The Delmarva peninsula hangs down from north to south, looking on the charts something like a bunch of grapes, its stem near the headwaters of the Chesapeake Bay and the Delaware River. The western edge of this peninsula is known as the Eastern Shore.

This is not as peculiar as it sounds. The colonial settlers of Maryland and Virginia lived on the west side of the Bay, in places like Baltimore, Annapolis, and Williamsburg. The Bay was vital to them for the shipping of all their supplies and also for transportation. It seemed natural to them to call its farther boundary the Eastern Shore. Many Marylanders have reduced this to "The Shore," or, as often, "The Sho'."

They say that this particular part of the coastal plain has been under water more than once; there are even some geologists who predict that it may submerge again. Like peninsular Florida, which has also risen from the sea more than once, there are few if any rocky shores to hold the land intact from the rampages of wind and surf. Muddy riverbanks and marshy borders wash away quickly in this tidewater country. Some small islands have disappeared entirely.

Slow-running rivers with old Indian names—Choptank, Pokomoke, and Wicomico—thread through the drowned meadows. The Miles River is an ancient contraction of St. Michael's. Down these barely moving streams float rafts of ruddy ducks; in their inlets and 82

coves rest migrating green-winged and blue-winged teal. On the dying oaks, uprooted by eroding banks, hunched-up turkey vultures watched for what might be washed in by the sluggish tide. A few of them soared overhead, rising on the thermals and casting their shadows over the cornfields where pheasants strolled and field larks perched on fence posts.

In the oak woods behind the pine-needle lanes where whippoor-wills sat in the dust at the road edges and the honeysuckle smelled sweet at night, red-bellied woodpeckers chattered at their holes. Tufted titmice wheezed in the tulip trees, and in the clipped box-wood gardens of the river houses, mourning doves cried over and over, *coo-a-roo, roo, roo.* Close by, mockingbirds scolded and chased the boat-tailed grackles that swept too close to their nests in the ivy on the chimneys.

Here and there along the Bay, narrow, spindly wharves reached into the water. Beside them some of the skipjacks of the oyster fleet were tied up. These single-masted sailing ships called skipjacks are the last commercial boats to work under sail in this country, and there are less than fifty of them left. Oystermen dredge and rake the oysters, and they think of the Bay as a tree, with all the rivers and tributaries as branches and stems. The towns along those rivers and tributaries have many a street made of crushed oyster shells.

It was in 1607 when Captain John Smith sailed into "Chesapeack Bay." And he paid it and its environs a lasting tribute: "There is but one entrance by Sea into this Country, and that is at the mouth of a very goodly Bay . . . Within is a country that may have the prerogative over the most pleasant places knowne . . . heaven and earth never agreed better to frame a place for man's habitation."

Checkerback and his turnstone companions hopped up on the rounded pyramids of gray-white oyster shells, long since pried open and cast aside, and pushed some of the loose shells about, hoping for a bit of the oyster muscle that might remain inside. But the gulls had been there first; not a morsel was left.

Across the "goodly Bay" and guarding the harbor of Baltimore, stood still another of the fortresses that had marked Checkerback's journey. Fort McHenry has a particular kind of fame. In August 1814, a British fleet churned up the Bay and into the Patuxent River. From there the armies marched on to Washington which they set afire. Dolley Madison, the President's wife, rescued a portrait of George Washington from the White House, but not much more.

Baltimore was the next target, and anxious Baltimoreans were prepared, even for conquest, but by the dawn's early light our banner's broad stripes and bright stars could be seen streaming over the ramparts of Fort McHenry. Francis Scott Key, a Marylander imprisoned on the British man-o'-war *Minden,* engaged in bombarding the

harbor, was so thankful and inspired to see the flag still flying that he composed what later became our national anthem. The Chesapeake campaign ended soon afterward, and a few months after that, the War of 1812.

Checkerback, however, was far in time and space from "the second war of independence." With wave after wave of migrating shorebirds, he stood on the great beach of the far-eastern arm of Cape Cod, ruffling his feathers and poking his head into them, confronting the wind. That meant facing the ocean. Almost at his firmly planted orange feet the ocean rolled up the flotsam and jetsam of the sea, a shred of kelp, a few broken shells, bits of beveled glass, cork and wood—all of these—caught in the net of foam that covered the rippled beach for a moment and then was absorbed or blown away.

Sanderlings fled stiff-legged before each lacy edge, as if they feared at any moment the wave might drown them. The next second they were back probing the wet sand. Suddenly they would rise like a plume of spray over the rough water, where now and then a wary willet would dash by, on flashing wings, calling its *pill-will-willet.* The black-bellied plovers, not as sociable as the other birds, stood apart under the high dunes of the beach where dusty miller with its velvety, pale gray foliage, and dune goldenrod and sea lav-

ender and beach pea engage in a constant struggle to catch a foothold in the unstable sand.

The dune or seaside goldenrod had adapted itself for a life quite different from its inland-field and meadow cousins by becoming a succulent, with fleshy stems to store water. It is still hard for us to think of a beach as a dry place, but as far as a plant is concerned available water for its use is scarce indeed in sandy habitats. Therefore xerophytes, those plants of dry soils, have had to make such changes as growing smaller leaves to reduce evaporation, and roots long enough either to reach the underground water table or to spread just below the surface for great distances.

Beach grass, a true xerophyte, that bends in the wind and with its bladelike edge carves arcs and circles in the sand, is also a great collector of the sand. In a way, it is thanks to the beach grass that the dunes do not disappear entirely. With its shallow, wide-spreading roots it anchors the sand hills and keeps them from blowing away.

Woolly *Hudsonia,* that yellow-blossoming beach heather, also carpets the dunes in sunny places. Like the dusty miller, it has velvety foliage which makes it less susceptible to water evaporation than plants with smooth or glossy leaves, like those in the tropical rain forests.

In the lee of the dunes, barely protected from the full blast of ocean wind and wave, prickly thickets of *Rosa rugosa,* or salt-spray

rose, bayberry, and beach plum form protective shelters for both migrating and resident land birds. And shorebirds too may fall exhausted into these, the first coverts they see, when blown in from the open water. In summer and fall the coral-colored rose hips of *rugosa* make nourishing meals for returning migrants.

Behind the dunes, delicate bearberry carpets the hollows reaching away from the sea toward the pitch-pine groves with their needled floors where deer and foxes walk without a sound. From a branch of one of the taller pines, a red-shouldered hawk, whose particular territory this was, rose with a shriek and circled over the woods, startling a flock of jays which took up the raucous crying they indulge in when mobbing an owl. Crows wheeled off their roosts and flapped out over the flooded cranberry bogs. The rabbit that the hawk had spotted plunged in the nick of time under the drumming log of a ruffed grouse. The hen grouse sat on her eggs not a yard away, at the base of a gray birch, and she moved not a muscle. So perfectly did the grouse and nest blend with last year's fallen leaves that neither rabbit nor hawk saw them at all.

Checkerback, in the course of his journeys, had heard many hawks. Whether or not they caught their rabbits was of little concern to him. He shuffled around in a rim of dried wrack at the high tide line, with his stout bill popping the air bladders that kept the plant floating upright in the water, rooting in the "holdfasts" of kelp and the openings in sponges for whatever tiny animals might be hiding there.

Yellowlegs, plovers, and sandpipers in tremendous numbers were feeding on the sand. Others simply walked along, looking out to sea. It hardly seemed that there could be enough food to satisfy them all, even on the "great beach."

The first person that we know of to call it by that name was a writer, philosopher, naturalist, and walker. He was born over a hundred and fifty years ago, but there are a few places where he is still a living presence. One is Walden Pond, and another is the outermost beach of Cape Cod.

In 1849, Henry David Thoreau tore himself away from his beloved Concord woods and made his first journey to the beach. He was to return twice after that. With a poet's sensitivity and a naturalist's attention to detail, although still indulging in some of the ramblings of a journalist, Thoreau recorded his impressions of the Cape. He wrote that he found the sandy stretches wild and rank, and perhaps after the luxuriant inland forests he had known they did indeed seem to him to be "the dreariest scenery imaginable." He went on to declare that "the barren aspect of the land would hardly be believed. The solitude was that of the ocean and the desert combined." Nevertheless he admired the "various beautiful forms and

colors of the sand," and, speaking like a true hermit, he did admit, "A man may stand there and put all America behind him."

The wind continued to blow and the beach grasses continued to bend their sharp tips and describe interlocking circles in the sand. Gathering birds, with their starlike tracks, moved over these circles, making the beach resemble a gigantic astronomy chart. Checkerback was glad to come upon a rusted anchor, thrusting up one of its flukes in the tide. Barnacles and clinging periwinkles sometimes provided a bite to eat.

The outermost beach of Cape Cod has now been made a national seashore. The National Park Service of our Department of the Interior has designated it as a kind of monument to wilderness. The sea and the wind may change it, and certainly will; but, by federal proclamation, man may not tamper with its "barren aspect," or encroach to any defacing extent upon Thoreau's solitude that "was that of the ocean and the desert combined." It is reassuring to know that there are those who remember what the hermit of Walden Pond also wrote: "In wildness is the preservation of the world."

The wind blew on and on with no sign of ceasing. Where it had sighed through the rippling palm fronds and the swaying ropes of Spanish moss on St. Simons, it now moved in against the stiffly rigid trunks of the stunted pitch pines. Only the contour of the trunks, bent and twisted away from the sea, indicated the power of this force.

The wind that had built and shaped and then reshaped the dunes, and rippled their slopes or whisked the sand off their peaks in a veil, and then, over the centuries, had blown them away and built new ones, sent a sudden gust of sand against Checkerback. Knocked momentarily off balance, his wings trailed in the sand and a little grainy rim settled around him.

"To see the earth in a grain of sand," wrote William Blake, poet and mystic. And who has not, in the idleness of a summer day, rubbed a grain between his thumb and finger and wondered what it was, and where it came from, and what would ultimately happen to it?

Sand is bound to be one of the oldest substances in the world. For one thing, it has taken eons of time to make it. Think of the grinding and polishing, the weathering and corroding, the disintegration and decay that have gone to form one single grain! In this condition, sand appears to have reached a state in which it is nearly indestructible. Cushioned by air or wetness, surrounded for the most part by other grains of more or less its own size, it is not likely to be reduced much further.

Some grains come originally from the land, from the granite rocks that create or underlie a coastline. Others come from the

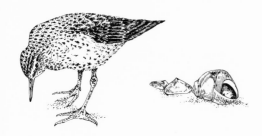

sea, from the minerals on the ocean's floor. Some are borne by the wind, blown hither and thither; others are washed in on long steady rollers. For all of its apparent heaviness and solidity when wet, sand is anything but an immobile substance. Grains of sand on a beach may change places a hundred times on a normal day, yet during that day the beach may not appear to have changed at all.

The sand on Checkerback's great outer beach had been ground from rock and minerals presumably pushed and crushed by creeping glaciers and splintered by glacial ice. Now, like ice, it glistened in the sun; minute particles of mica, quartz, and feldspar sent back pinpoint reflections. There were times when the light seemed to dazzle the birds. They stood like statues over their shadows and closed their eyes.

The sun went down, and as it did it was almost as if it had taken the wind with it. The sudden lull resembled the quiet in the center of a hurricane, when the eye passes over. It had a marked effect on the birds. No longer did they stand still, fluffed out, protecting themselves from the cold. Instead they hurried about, probing their bills into the sand and the mud flats and the salt marshes. The great beach was all at once a flurry of activity.

Adding to this, fishermen, who had waited for the wind to die, strode in their hip boots down the paths they had made between the dunes, and hopefully cast their lines into the surf that was still roiled and churned. Their bait buckets made circles in the wet sand. Checkerback eyed them, and a longing stirred inside of him. But a stronger longing told him that it was time to go. His flock was moving restlessly. The wind had fallen and night was falling too. Once again the ruddy turnstone took off on his long migration.

Night Flight

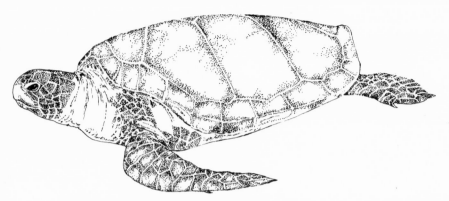

NIGHT FELL slowly on the beach the birds were leaving. On the black sands of Martinique, indeed throughout the tropics, darkness comes much more quickly. Close to the equator it seems almost instantaneous. But further north, in any season of the year, twilights are less abrupt and last much longer.

Dune grasses and pitch pine stood in silhouette against the red sky of sunset. The fishermen, their poles over their shoulders, their wet lines shining in the protracted light, began to trudge back from the waves, which had flattened now that the wind had died.

Milling around in the shallows was a pair of horseshoe crabs. They are not really crabs at all, but related to spiders and scorpions. Changing very little over the past four hundred million years, horseshoe crabs have been called living fossils. The female was getting ready to come ashore to lay her eggs in the sand.

The sea turtle is another animal which has not yet made the complete transition from one environment to another. Miles away to the south, the great female turtles were lumbering from the phosphorescent surf onto the flat coral beaches to lay their eggs in a scoop made by their fins in the dry sand. The full moon of May is sometimes called the "turtle moon" where the greens and the loggerheads and the hawkbills come ashore to deposit their eggs. Painstakingly covered with sand, the eggs are then left alone to be hatched by the warmth of the sun.

Not all of them make it, by any means. Piles of torn white shells, rubbery and empty, bear witness to a raid by a hungry raccoon or other predator. Just as often the raids are made by humans, and they leave no empty shells, only their footprints. Turtle eggs, in some countries, are regarded as gourmet delicacies. There is, then, well-justified concern about the future of the sea turtle. Although as far back as 1620 Bermuda passed a law against the killing of "tortoyses," which even then were regarded as a delicacy, two hundred years later, Audubon, cruising through the Florida Keys, wrote in his journal that "great numbers are killed by turtlers and Indians, as well as by cougars, lynxes, bears and wolves."

No turtles crawled ashore under the May moon on the Cape Cod beach from which Checkerback and his companions had departed on the last lap of their migration. But there were other night roamers. Muskrats crept out from the reeds to nose in the sea wrack. Fearful, foraging mice and shrews left dainty tracks. Raccoons searched for shellfish in the darkness. Sometimes a white-tailed deer wandered across the salt marshes from its forest home, spotlighted for an instant in the golden beam of the lighthouse.

Aside from that shaft of warning light, and the port and starboard signals of offshore draggers and trawlers and freighters, there was no artificial light visible from the great beach. Yet even on a moonless night, a beach is never dark the way a forest or even a desert is dark. The sea seems to hold a radiance of its own. This radiance is often caused by phosphorescence. Herring fishermen sometimes discover their schools of fish by hitting the sides of their skiffs with their oars and seeing the water light up when the herring jump at the sound. In moving, the fish knock against tiny soft globules of plankton, called *noctilucas,* or "night lights," which glow when touched. Swim in a plankton-filled sea and you will find yourself outlined with light. Hold the jelly-bean-sized night lights in your palm and you can see and feel them. Moon jellies, those larger symmetrically patterned coelenterates, gleam softly as they drift or pulsate through the currents.

And then, of course, the ocean itself, that lively mirror of the heavens, reflects the lights of the night sky: stars, planets, moon, and luminous clouds. It is only under this lucent surface that true darkness begins. Starlight, even moonlight, cannot penetrate far.

That darkness is one of the reasons why oceanography is among our later scientific studies. Another reason is the weight of the tons of water pressing down; and then there has always been the lack of available oxygen. But with the conquest of high mountains, and with research stations established at both poles, most of the Earth's surface has now been explored. The moon's dark side has been photographed, and man is ready to land there. That leaves two com-

pelling regions for exploration: interplanetary space and the depths of the sea.

Space flights have captured our imagination: astronauts have become our heroes. Until very recently, journeys to the bottom of the sea do not seem to have stirred us as much. But now huge companies are developing what they call "submersibles," pressurized and lighted diving ships in which several divers can probe the depths twenty thousand feet below the surface.

Weather satellites circle the globe, giving reports of cloud cover. Soon a globe-girdling satellite for oceanography may be perfected. Men in sea-scanning spacecraft could, with radar and other instruments, peer into the depths of oceans more than one hundred miles below them.

Before William Beebe, that pioneer explorer of the underwater world, descended in 1934 in his famous bathysphere, people believed that nothing at all could be seen lower than two hundred and fifty feet beneath the surface. Eye to eye with the inhabitants of the coral reefs off Bermuda, Beebe claimed that he could make out swimming shapes in depths up to two thousand feet. And he added: "Until we have found our way to some other planet, the bottom of the sea will have to remain the loveliest and strangest place we can imagine."

Actually most living organisms in the ocean do exist in a 250-foot 96

layer from the surface down; like the icing on a cake it is a very small percentage of the whole. But beyond the point where sunlight can penetrate, green plants cannot grow, and without green plants most animals cannot exist. A sun shining down from high overhead lights the ocean longer and more deeply than does a sun low on the horizon. So tropic waters, like tropic jungles, support more plant and animal life than polar seas are able to.

Where Checkerback was flying with his flock of turnstones, moonlight fell on a sea that was neither tropical nor polar. The rocky coast and islands of Maine were dotted with lighthouses, so that from a bird's-eye view the shoreline appeared as if lighted like a highway. It was indeed a kind of highway—a flyway for millions of birds.

Migration, or the periodic seasonal movement of animals from one place to another, usually for the purpose of breeding, has fascinated men since biblical times. Job asked: "Doth the hawk fly by Thy wisdom, and stretch her wings toward the south?" Jeremiah wrote that "the stork in the heavens knoweth her appointed time; and the turtle, and the crane, and the swallow, observe the time of their coming." Even blind Homer understood about the cranes "which flee from the coming winter and sudden rain, and fly with clamor towards the streams of the ocean."

Aristotle too wrote about cranes and other birds moving south-ward with the advent of cold weather, and Pliny the Elder was concerned with the disappearance and reappearance of his European blackbirds and thrushes. But these men, as well as a great many others down through the centuries, had only vague and fantastic ideas about where the birds spent the intervening time. Doves, storks, and swifts, as well as swallows, were believed to burrow into mud where they rolled themselves into little balls and hibernated through the winter. Olaus Magnus, in 1555, published a "scientific" treatise in which he described swallows caught in the nets drawn up by fishermen. And until the wintering grounds of the chimney swift were finally discovered within the past twenty-five years, there were some bird watchers who still persisted in adhering to the "mud theory."

An Englishman "of Learning and Piety" in the eighteenth century published a pamphlet stating that migratory birds spent their winters on the moon. Other observers maintained that small birds who would have difficulty completing long journeys, crossed the waters on the backs of larger birds. Throngs of shore birds feeding on the flats were believed to be waiting for pelicans, storks, and cranes to transport them.

And then there was the belief, originated by no one less than the philosopher and naturalist Aristotle, that migrating species 98

were "transmuted," or transformed, into resident species for the duration of the winter, assuming different shapes and plumages to enable them to survive in the cold. With the coming of spring they would change back.

It is all very well for us to scoff at these naïve ideas, but the mystery of migration is still far from being solved. The search for the answers to the many riddles in this field continues to occupy the time and intrigue the minds of ornithologists. Why do birds migrate? How do they know when it is time to go? How do they find their way? It is no wonder that migration has been called a "mysterious planetary phenomenon."

Actually birds are not the only animals that migrate. Monarch butterflies make long and spectacular migrations. In brilliant orange-and-black swarms, and on fragile paperlike wings, they have traveled from Canada to the Gulf Coast. One banded monarch made the 1,870-mile journey from Ontario to San Luis Potosí, Mexico, in four months and a week.

Alewives run up rivers to spawn. Salmon make that famous migration from the inland streams where they were hatched to the open sea, and then back to the same river mouth, and at last, even up waterfalls, to the identical spawning ground. It seems as unbelievable as the Ascension Island finding of the green turtles four thousand miles away from their Brazilian home.

As early as 1684 an Italian observer by the name of Francesco Redi described the migration of eels, the adults' journey from fresh water to the sea to deposit eggs, and the ultimate return of the young to fresh water. Great masses of floating seaweed in the Sargasso Sea provide protection for the incubation of millions and millions of eel eggs, and unending nourishment for the larvae before they begin to follow the wide Atlantic currents.

Some bats make long night flights, feeding on the wing as they go. With their poor eyesight, bats depend upon high-frequency sonar signals to keep them from knocking into walls and branches. This same built-in radar allows them to catch all the insects they need in their darting, erratic maneuvers.

Caribou make a tremendous migration, from the Arctic tree-line and the damp muskeg, north to that great empty plain called the Barren Grounds, often crossing waterways choked with ice to do so. Reindeer range north as the ice melts, seeking the lichens and so-called reindeer moss on which they graze. On the western plains, bison move in huge circular patterns.

Many tales have been written about the lemmings, those little mouselike creatures of Arctic regions, that make a one-way mass migration and never come back. They multiply so rapidly that naturalists once believed that they had fallen from the sky, overnight, like snow. Periodically there are too many of them for the available food supply. In these "lemming years," which occur about one year in four, they must, like all other members of the animal kingdom, move on or perish.

In the case of the lemming, moving on also means perishing. In their wild dash, during which they seem to ignore available food, they sweep over the land like a brown, undulating river. And they become all too easy targets for swooping snowy owls and starving Arctic foxes and wolves. Fish devour them as they traverse lakes and streams. Eventually those that survive come to the sea and in they plunge. Not one returns. Only the few who have remained behind on the tundra are left to begin the cycle all over again.

Fortunately the lemming migration, which is actually not a true migration at all, is unique. Most of the other animals that migrate do find their way back.

The question arises: How do we know that the same migrant returns to the same location? A bluebird flies out of the spring sky one morning and goes straight to a hole in a gnarled apple tree where a bluebird nested the previous April. But how can we say whether or not it is the identical bird? How dare we state that a butterfly turning up on a milkweed plant in Mexico had left Canada four months before? The answer is in banding.

To many people the banding of a butterfly is as remarkable a

feat as the migration itself. How can it possibly be done? They are thinking of a ring around the insect's leg.

Butterfly banding, or tagging as it is usually called, is accomplished by the gluing of a tiny numbered scrap of paper over the lower edge of one wing. The butterfly is caught in a net, held gently in the hand, tagged amid much fluttering, and released. The monarch then flaps a bit awkwardly to a nearby branch or leaf, spreads out its wings as if to dry them, rests, and almost at once is off on its way, apparently unhampered by the identifying tag. At its destination, and along the way, the tag is read by observers with nets, and the number is recorded and reported.

Birdbanding, or ringing, is quite different. On a mild day in 1803, exactly one hundred years after the person "of Learning and Piety" had published his theory of birds' migrating to the moon, John James Audubon sat beside an insect-haunted brook at his Mill Grove, Pennsylvania, home and watched a pair of phoebes feeding their young in a nest under a stone bridge. He wondered whether they were the same birds that had been there the summer before. Did birds come back to their last year's nest? To find out, he twisted thin wire in a loose circle around a leg of each nestling. The next spring a phoebe arrived and poked around the brookside nest. It wore a wire circle on its leg.

Actually, the first record we have a birdbanding is of a heron

ringed in Turkey in 1730. Since then banding has come far. On every continent licensed observers capture birds in window traps, pole traps, or water traps, or in nearly invisible "mist nets," made of fine silky thread. They band, record, and release them. Sometimes, instead of being banded, the birds are marked by dipping them in nontoxic dye, or painting their wings or legs, or attaching colored feathers. In the Chesapeake Bay, whistling swans are caught in floating funnel traps, dyed, kept in the cages overnight to let the color dry, and then released. Along other coasts swans are dyed in different colors to indicate the location. It is all done for the same purpose: to help solve the mystery of migration.

Audubon's famous phoebes migrated by night, resting and fly-catching during the day. Checkerback and all turnstones—in fact, most shorebirds, flycatchers, wrens, thrushes, warblers, sparrows, and other small birds—make nocturnal migrations. They use the precious daylight hours to look for the crustaceans, insects, seeds, and other food that they might not be able to see at night.

How in the world do they find their way in the dark? The logical answer might seem at first thought to be by moonlight or starlight. But the moon is luminous enough for clear visibility only several nights each month, and many of these nights may be overcast. Clouds and fog can hide recognizable constellations. Light-

houses mark coastal flyways, but over the open ocean there are no lighthouses. And, of course, to the birds that have never made the journey, lights and other visible clues could have no significance.

To try to solve this riddle of how migrants know where they are going when they cannot see landmarks, or are traveling for the first time, some scientists have suggested that the earth's magnetic field may lead them, acting upon a highly specialized and sensitive organ in the bird's eye. They have also considered the Coriolis force which affects air currents as the earth rotates on its axis, and perhaps therefore affects the flights of birds.

Observers have even wondered whether an older, experienced migrant might not lead the young birds, but except for geese, ducks, and swan, and other species that fly in V formation or in skeins, this premise does not seem likely. As a matter of fact, many flocks of inexperienced migrants fly south without any adults in the group at all.

So far, most naturalists have had to be content with the vague explanation called the "homing instinct," that innate compulsion most easily and directly observed in homing pigeons. In the case of migration, birds seem to have inherited not only the desire but also the ability to return to their homes.

Unlike Checkerback and other shorebirds, not all birds choose to fly by night. Those that make daytime, or diurnal, migrations

are usually larger birds with strong, powerful wings, birds that are able to cross wide plains and mountain ranges. Fortunately for us, two of the most thrilling sights in bird migration occur by daylight hours: a long V of geese against a dawn or sunset sky, and a boiling cloud of hawks—which usually travel singly—rising on a thermal from behind a peak and swirling down over an autumn valley. Geese may also fly by dark; who has not heard their honking at midnight?

Some birds make what is called a "vertical" or "altitudinal" migration, seeking the coolness of a high mountaintop for breeding and then descending to their winter homes in valleys which may be only a few thousand feet below. Juncos, chickadees, pine siskins, some pipits and wood pewees may save hundreds of days and miles compared with birds on latitudinal migrations.

Evening grosbeaks make east-west migrations, breeding in northwest Canada and turning up in New England in the wintertime. Redhead ducks migrate from Utah and Nebraska to the Chesapeake Bay. And then there is the "loop" migration that the Australian muttonbird, a shearwater, makes from Tasmania to the Bering Sea and back down the Pacific coast and across the ocean to Tasmania again.

But it is the long migration that seems to have captured our imagination most of all. The golden plover flies a distance of over two thousand miles without ever once stopping to rest or feed. It

is a journey over the ocean, from Canada to South America. The return trip is over land; thus we can say that the plover makes a sort of loop migration too.

The Arctic tern, though, wins all the prizes for long distance flight. No other animal, even the whale, travels so far. Crossing the Atlantic, flying nearly from pole to pole, and nearly always under the shining sun, the Arctic tern finds its way twenty-five thousand miles around the world. It is a temptation to call the small, black-capped, swallow-tailed water bird brave, or adventurous, or foolhardy. But the bird is simply following out the pattern of its existence. In spite of all the dangers, discomforts, and uncertainties, migration is as natural to a migratory animal as feeding and breeding.

The full moon, which may or may not aid the birds in their nocturnal migrations, does give aid to their observers. Across its bright face, migrating flocks are counted by earthbound bird watchers peering through "spotting scopes" and binoculars. They think of the moon's face as the face of a clock; they mark it off in hours as if it were numbered; and they call out, "Bird passing from four to nine!" Some of these observers have noticed that more turnstones tend to fly on moonlight nights, and that some even appear to wait for the full moon.

Moon-watch data is only one contribution to the continuing

study of avian navigation and orientation. Navigation concerns the techniques of flying, orientation the methods of direction-finding. Together they make up the area of the most intensive research.

That birds have a strong and almost infallible sense of direction even under the most thwarting conditions has been proven again and again. One of the earliest tests was made when sooty and noddy terns from the Dry Tortugas, carried by ship in cages below deck, and released eight hundred miles from home, managed to find their way back to their nests on the coral sand. Homing pigeons, enrolled in racing contests by their owners, are sent in crates on closed freight cars to release points a thousand miles away. It is a rare occurrence when every bird does not return to its cote.

Scientists in helicopters, following the pigeons, have made some important observations and contributions to the subjects of navigation and orientation. They have found that birds do appear to use the earth's magnetic field, and that their diurnal flight paths tend to be influenced by landmarks and other visual clues such as coastlines and riverbeds.

They have discovered that some birds tend to fly into or over high objects. Canada geese will make a turn to pass directly above a television tower; pigeons will go out of their way to fly over the tallest tree in a grove. Why should they do this? Scientists say that the earth's magnetic field is disturbed in such places, and the lines of force are redirected. Tall objects are more highly charged—we

have all heard of lightning striking the highest point because of the high conductivity there—and these project an electric current or charge which draws birds like a magnet.

Sometimes it draws them to their destruction. It is well known that tall structures present great hazards to birds. In a single night thousands of them, mostly thrushes, warblers, and vireos, were killed on a migration through Wisconsin. Their bodies were found at the base of a television tower.

Radar, as well as aircraft, is used to spot, count, and follow migrating birds. While not always accurate in reflecting numbers, radar is vital in indicating direction and speed of flight, and the influence of the wind. Both nocturnal and diurnal migrants make use of favoring winds. It is believed that they can detect ground turbulence at relatively high altitudes, and sometimes will fly into adverse winds if they must in order to maintain their route. When these opposing winds cause the birds to drift off their "compass course" they are able to redirect themselves. Also in adverse winds, birds often fly faster, compensating for opposition.

Both terrestrial and celestial clues help to keep avian migrants on their remarkable compass courses. Time-lapse photography is used for plotting migration routes. By this method it has been discovered that some flocks passing over the Atlantic tend to veer inward toward land, whereas birds flying over land make more

direct flights to their destinations. And the flocks that do turn inward toward land will straighten out their courses on reaching it, and fly parallel to the routes they maintained over the ocean.

In general small birds migrate at night at heights of around one thousand feet. They keep the flock together by frequent chirping and calling. Nearly as many may fly anywhere between five hundred and fifteen hundred feet, but close to two thousand feet the numbers dwindle. Most water fowl migrate quite high, usually above fifteen hundred feet.

Many birds prefer to fly low because of the greater density, and therefore greater buoyancy, of the air. Sometimes fog, lowering clouds, or mountain ranges force migrants to fly higher than their usual altitudes. Naturally, the higher the bird flies, the more of the earth's surface it can see. It has been estimated that on a fine day a bird flying at five hundred feet can look down on twenty-seven miles of ground, whereas a bird soaring at two thousand feet sees fifty-five miles of the earth below. While to a migrant at high altitudes individual landmarks and clues may seem to disappear, helpful patterns of coastline, mountain range, and riverbed undoubtedly extend.

Just how much the temperature affects migration is not definitely known. Most birds do move to a warmer climate with the approach of cool weather, but, on the other hand, there are many species that do not migrate at all. The ruffed grouse spends its entire life

not far from its drumming log in a leafy wood. English sparrows seem content with the backyards or city parks where they flourish. Bobwhites and cardinals tend to stay put. On the other hand, some blue jays and crows, which may seem to be permanent residents, are actually replaced by others of their species, slipping in and out with the seasons. Some robins will overwinter in a sheltered northern woods. Seasonal change does not seem to bother them.

Each year it is reported in the news that the well-known swallows have returned on schedule to the California mission of Capistrano. St. Joseph's Day, the nineteenth of March, is the anticipated arrival date, no matter how severe the winter or how early the spring. Actually their arrival may vary by as much as a week or two.

In an experiment of great imagination and delicacy, feather-weight radios were attached to the legs of thrushes. Tracked by such radio tagging, the birds were reported to migrate more readily in warm temperatures, particularly those over seventy degrees. Radio tracking is still in its infancy. It has been employed with varying success on green turtles in their migrations. Birds have not sent clear signals much further than two hundred miles; long distance broadcasting is still to come.

During the winter months, most birds feed and rest, in a sense preparing themselves for the long journey ahead. With the coming of spring, the impulse to undertake the journey and ultimately to

mate and reproduce becomes irresistibly strong. Rising temperature and humidity, lengthening daylight, and favorable winds all play their parts as stimuli to send the birds on their way. Birds in training cages feel the same stimuli and impulses.

This is one of the most fascinating of the orientation studies. Think of a sparrow, confined in a wire-mesh cage, with no expectation of release, becoming restless at the time of its normal migratory season, and hopping nervously about, clawing at the wire. Think of this same sparrow clawing at the north side of its cage in spring, and at the south side in autumn. Ornithologists have observed this remarkable behavior time after time.

Or imagine an ovenbird trapped in a planetarium. Experiments showed that the ovenbird tried to fly north when the lighted constellations of spring were displayed on the inside of the dome. Six months later, when the ceiling was turned to its autumn setting, the bird sought to migrate south, apparently reacting to the star patterns.

Under the star pattern of Cygnus, the swan, the constellation that seems to float like a great migrant bird with wings outspread in the Milky Way, Checkerback flew on and on. His urgency to reach his destination grew by the hour, and the tundra was almost in sight.

Tundra World

THE NAME comes from a word akin to the Finnish *tunturi,* which means a "treeless plain," or an "Artic hill," according to the translation. Beyond the edges of the northern forest where the brief summers are lighted twenty-four hours by the midnight sun, and the winters are long and dark and frigid, there stretches a wild country of heath and lichen and stunted Arctic shrubs. Some of the land is flat; some is rolling; all is dotted with bogs, streams, and ponds, usually frozen fast. In late spring, the sun is sufficiently warm to melt a few inches of the permafrost, that almost permanently frozen layer of soil or subsoil. Then reindeer, caribou, and ptarmigan come to drink the ice water in the little mirroring ponds and to feed on the fresh growth of sedges and willows at the water's edge.

Since glacial times, the ground a short distance beneath the surface has been perpetually frozen. This makes hibernation on the tundra virtually impossible, which in turn automatically eliminates the reptiles that prey on nesting birds. The melting of the ice produces greatly needed moisture for all the animals and plants. Rainfall in the tundra is light in the growing season; most of the precipitation falls during the winter as snow. And with the melting of the ice a profusion of brilliantly colored wild flowers bursts forth, and with them a myriad of insects. All of these factors, and its vast extent, make the tundra an ideal nesting place for the

thousands and thousands of shorebirds that make the long journey.

It is the midnight sun, though, that makes life on the tundra possible. Without it hovering above the pole during the round-the-clock daylight of an Arctic summer, plants and animals could not exist at all, let alone store what they need for the months ahead, the long winter or the long migration.

The land we call the tundra is circumpolar, and its borders follow the irregular, sprawling tree line rather than the regular curve the mapmakers call the Arctic Circle and draw on globes at sixty-six degrees, thirty-three minutes. Actually most of the tundra of North America lies north of fifty-seven degrees, between the tree line and the snow line.

Temperature, of course, defines most realistically the limits of the treeless plain. Between the short summer warmth that averages less than fifty degrees, and the deep low that has been measured at a mean of minus fifty-eight degrees during the coldest month in Siberia, the temperature sets the timberline more or less at the isotherm, or line of heat, where the warmest month, July, reaches an average of fifty degrees.

Temperatures do not change abruptly at isoterms, nor do trees automatically disappear at a tree line. The transition is gradual. First they become dried and twisted by wind blasts and bent from the weight of the snow, then stunted and diminished by lack of sunlight

and loss of available nutrients in the soil, until gradually there are no trees at all to speak of. A few may linger where there are moderating seas and sheltering valleys, but little by little the scrub willows and dwarf birches and alders take over, and finally the shallow-rooted plants are all that remain to gain a foothold above the impenetrable permafrost.

All through the long months of winter the tundra had lain in darkness and cold. Snowfall after snowfall had mounded up upon frozen lake and laden bush and the snow burrows of animals. Polar bears, their seal hunting over, slept in their dens near the seacoast; rock ptarmigan roosted eight inches deep. Many of the insects had begun their hibernations as early as the end of September and had endured January temperatures of minus fifty degrees. Aquatic insects had buried themselves, before the surface started to freeze, in the shallow mud of ponds and bogs.

Lemmings bred in their runways under the drifts, increasing their numbers for their one-way migrations. In bitterly cold winters of little snow, lemmings have been known to freeze to death from exposure. Then the snowy owl, their chief predator, is driven miles to the south to hunt by daylight and perch, with its warm feathered feet, like a snow carving on a frosty New England hayrick.

No night, not even a polar night, is ever completely black. Indeed

the total Arctic night of the winter solstice gleams softly, when the skies are clear, with starlight reflected on ice. Aurora borealis shimmers in luminous curtains or flares up toward the top of the sky in ribbons of red or blue-green or white. "Northern lights" are believed to be caused by tremendous explosions on the sun's surface, and occur most often when a giant sunspot appears. The earth's magnetic field attracts these auroras and concentrates their glow near the magnetic poles. Some polar explorers even claim to have heard the sky crackle as the streamers rippled up.

Full moonlight on fresh snow can have a sparkling quality that dazzles the eye. And, just like the sun in the brief summer, the full moon in the depths of the Arctic winter also circles the horizon without setting.

What does it shine down upon? Most of the birds have left. Even the ptarmigan, remarkably hardy and protectively transformed from heath-brown to snow-white in coloration, moves slightly south-ward to browse on alder and willow buds and whatever low vegetation the gales have not covered with snowdrifts. Owls hunt silently on the wing, soaring and then pouncing on an incautious lemming or white-furred Arctic hare that has ventured from its burrow for an instant nibble of lichen or bark or twigs. An occasional raven croaks above the wind.

Restless caribou stalk for miles in search of lichen or "reindeer moss." Moose and musk ox munch willows along gelid streams.

Snow-white Arctic foxes feast on the ptarmigan they have caught earlier and preserved beneath the snow until needed; they understood the usefulness of frozen food long before we did. The ranging white Arctic wolf comes not only upon the lemming's burrow, but upon the lemming and its stored-up food supply as well. The winter moon looks down on an old and endless story: the hunter and the hunted, the seeking and the hiding, the shout of triumph coupled with the scream of fear.

Now it was June and the Arctic night was well over. Summer, in fact, had burst upon the land. Its most obvious manifestation, the wildflowers, carpeted peat and heath and muskeg. Birdsong began about two in the morning; some birds sang all night long.

Night that meant darkness was a thing of the past. Each of the twenty-four hours offered a molten, changing light. The sky slipped almost imperceptibly from sapphire to deep orange, hot pink, pale apricot, and salmon, banded by turquoise, amethyst, and gold. Night, as the arriving birds had known it earlier, was no more.

Patches of ice had remained well into April. The snow buntings, first to arrive, had found much of the ground still white. Their ptarmigan-feather-lined nests would not be started until the females appeared in May.

As the hours of daylight had lengthened, the caribou had begun their great spring trek to the polar shores from the sheltering forests just below the tree line. On pushed the urgent herds, band after band of marching animals, sometimes antler to antler. Now and then they paused to graze, and then pressed on, occasionally trampling the nests of longspur and ptarmigan, but avoiding the wolves, their perpetual enemies. The caribou were hurrying to reach the mosquito-free northern plains where their calves would be born.

Seals too had become active as the ice slowly turned to water; many of them have their pups in April. Some whales start their northward migrations as early as March, but walruses must wait until the ice breaks up before they can undertake their difficult journeys. Ducks and gulls, though, had already flocked to the open water off the coast.

During May the sweetly singing land birds of the Arctic summer had dropped down on beds of early-blossoming purple saxifrage and scattered patches of chickweed and yellow cinquefoil. But May is not flower time in the tundra; in fact, it has been said by some that there is no such thing as an Arctic spring.

Still the birds sang as birds sing on any spring day: redpolls with a whistled goldfinch-like call in flight, horned larks with their silvery bell-like tinkle often rung out in mid-air, Lapland longspurs pouring forth a bubbly trill on the wing, pipits performing

their elaborate flight songs from great elevations and then drifting to the ground as gently as a feather. In the treeless world of the tundra where there are few if any perches for singing, courtship song is often heard from on high. Incidentally, the absence of trees determines nesting habits too. The redpoll builds in a low bush, the snow bunting in a deep crevice; but most of the other thousands of birds that burst upon the Arctic each year construct their nests directly on the ground.

May had been over nearly three weeks ago. The annual migrations had poured their hordes onto their breeding grounds. Only a few species had not yet arrived. Among them was Checkerback. What had happened to the ruddy turnstones?

The answer indicates no cause for alarm. The turnstone nests in the northernmost part of the tundra, the part that is called the High Arctic, and the land up there was not yet through the winter.

The region called the High Arctic varies so drastically in climate from the southern, or low, Arctic that the wildlife there also has to be different. Since the winters are longer, darker, colder, and without much moderating and sheltering snow, very little vegetation can grow there. And without vegetation no animal can survive. As late as May, the land is a windy, moon-marked desert; it would be fatal for the turnstones to arrive then.

To be sure, a few migrating eider ducks and geese attempt to, but these are birds accustomed to such hazards and large enough to survive for several days without food if necessary.

Even so, they and those shorebirds that do try to come too soon have a hard time of it. Countless dunlins and black-bellied plovers perish from hunger and cold in a land not yet prepared for them. Others are battered by polar gales and driven far out to sea. More birds die from exposure in May than in any other Arctic month. It is pitiful to think of their having journeyed so far to meet such an end. Checkerback was well guided to postpone his arrival in the High Arctic until June.

And by June, even as far north as the turnstone's nesting ground, flowers were opening. As in the lower tundra, the purple saxifrage was the first. Its small starry flowers bloomed almost overnight. White heather and crowberry bloomed too, and if a rare light snowfall covered the plants from time to time it quickly melted in the pale slanting rays of the midnight sun.

Without a sound, Checkerback, the ruddy turnstone from the tropical shores of faraway Brazil, dropped down on a gravel beach not far from a patch of saxifrage where the ice had just melted. It was June and the turnstones had arrived at their breeding grounds in northwest Greenland. Most of the flock in which Checkerback traveled had successfully completed the trip. Now the birds rested,

and then, one by one, began rooting among the shiny streamers of seaweed which only a few days before had been encased as if in glass. The beach and the seaweed were cold underfoot; here and there in shady places splinters of ice still glimmered.

The birds fed as if they had not seen food for a long time. Checkerback threw up little fountains of gravel as he dug with his stocky beak among the drifts of rockweed and debris cast up by winter gales. He had not seen the Arctic since he had left it as a fledgling two years before. The past summer, not yet ready to mate, he had spent on the coast of Maine. Now that he was older, he was growing more and more aware of that other urgency, the one that had brought him so far and on so hazardous a journey. Rested and well fed, he turned all of his attention to finding a mate.

Many of his companions were already mated when they began their journey; some chose mates on the way. Even so, here on the gravelly shingle there were more males than females, and some of the males were fighting bitterly, and even to the death, for the females' approval. Checkerback, although inexperienced in the art and rivalry of courtship, was not inexperienced in warfare; turnstones are pugnacious by nature. Eager to mate, and unafraid to fight, he approached a female who was standing a bit apart from the others, apparently not yet claimed.

She appeared to be exhausted; her eye was not bright; she had

a dazed look, as if she were staring at something but not quite seeing it. In truth she was indeed exhausted and dazed. It had been her first northward migration too, and she had barely made it. Time after time only sheer fortitude had kept her from dropping into the sea. Her name was Calico, another fishermen's name for turnstones. When she saw Checkerback approaching, she gathered together her last remaining strength and skittered away.

It was all part of the courtship pattern. And up to that point she had not attracted much attention. Now two other males came toward her. In an instant the two were engaged in a fierce battle, dashing back and forth over the windrow, rising several feet in the air, pursuing one another in remarkable and sudden fury; then falling to the ground and taking up the fight as belligerently as before. Checkerback watched with a mixture of wonder and admiration, uncertain what to do next. Calico had shuffled away, and now stood at some distance, looking back with the same dazed expression.

The fighting turnstones rolled on down the beach like one ball of flying feathers. They seemed to have forgotten Calico, and thus, apparently, the very reason for their battle. As Checkerback turned to reassure himself of their whereabouts, a fourth male turnstone presented himself to Calico. With more energy than she had yet shown she dashed this way and that, avoiding the bird's advances.

Checkerback did not hesitate. With a fervor unsurpassed by the other two, he began a fight of his own; it was his first courtship combat. With one eye on Calico, he jabbed and clawed at his rival. Then, vanquishing him with a final thrust, he fluttered to a nearby rock and uttered a victorious *tchiwick, chirrup.* He had won his battle and his mate as well.

But Checkerback was not entirely through with rivals. More courting males showed up before Calico from time to time, and Checkerback was hard put to it to drive them away. Showing her lack of interest, Calico would wander off to feed. On her return, Checkerback fanned his tail in a welcoming gesture.

Then he started doing something he had never done before, and it was a strange sight. Sitting down in the moss, he pressed his breast into it and rubbed it this way and that until he had made a sort of hollow. It looked like a nest. He made several of these hollows, but Calico paid no attention to them. She was busy gathering leaves and stems and bits of dried seaweed to make a nest of her own. It was a soft shallow bowl, rimmed with blossoming heath and sheltered by a clump of rosy dwarf rhododendron. But not until she had laid her first glossy egg in it did Checkerback give up trying to form his own false nests.

Well recovered from the rigors of her journey, Calico laid four eggs. They were as smooth as china and colored a creamy buff

olive, marked at random with chocolate-brown spots and dark
green, gray, and violet streaks that ran across the shells like veins
in marble. During the few times that the nest was left untended,
the eggs were almost invisible, so perfectly did they blend with
their surroundings.

Calico and Checkerback took turns sitting on the eggs. Calico's
turns were usually at night, and longer than her mate's, because
Checkerback spent much of his time perched on a hummock or
a rocky outcropping close by, standing guard and driving off predators. Marauding jaegers and skuas, those hawklike birds of the
open seas, cruised hungrily by. They were far larger than Checkerback, but the turnstone had discovered his prowess in battle, and
particularly in nest defending. Crying angrily, he dashed out after
the big hunters, warding them off and routing them, and then
returning to wait for the next.

Sometimes the enemy was an Arctic fox. When one of these
was on the prowl, all the turnstones nesting in the vicinity would
unite to swoop down on it with screams of fury and fear.

July came, and with it full summer came to the Arctic. Birds
took full advantage of the twenty-four-hour sunlight to feed their
young with the myriads of insects: caddis flies, crane flies, and bees,
that had been emerging daily for some time. The flowering plants

also took advantage of the endless daylight to open in a vivid blanket of color; the whole tundra was now in bloom.

Dwarf rhododendron had spread its deep rose petals. Labrador tea blossomed white above its brown-lined leathery leaves. Andromeda, the bog rosemary, shook out the palest pink bells. And tiny wild orchids, pink and lavender and white, swayed on their delicate stems. All the lakes and ponds were now open and reflected a sky eternally bright. It would seem to be the ideal time to remain and enjoy the Arctic. But many birds were already preparing to leave on their southward migrations. The last to arrive were among the first to go.

Checkerback and Calico had safely hatched all of their eggs. Four downy young in various shades of cream and buff, spotted and striped in charcoal, sat in the shallow nest and quietly waited to be fed. At first they had just opened their mouths; each of them seemed to be nothing but mouth; later they assumed begging positions. Fortunately the teeming, prolific season of summer, brief though it was, provided enough to satisfy their incessant hunger. Checkerback and Calico spent nearly all of their time procuring food for them.

But Checkerback was still vitally engaged in chasing off predators. And Calico, when the birds were able to leave the nest, led them cautiously to damp feeding places, sheltered by bushy heath

125

or rock piles, and hovered close to them except when an enemy
appeared. Then she would flap her wings wildly and cry shrilly to
attract attention to herself and away from her brood. Sometimes
she would even feign injury, and limp away through the grasses,
trailing a "broken" wing. In times like these she might well have
been killed, and her young with her, had not Checkerback and other
fighting males been there.

By mid-July a change was evident in the tundra. The peak of
summer was past; the longest day had occurred almost a month
ago. Some birds had already left, and there was also a diminishing
of the marine and insect food supply. Before long there would not
be sufficient for the hordes of growing young. Checkerback and
Calico saw their fledglings gaining in size and strength, and needing
more nourishment.

By now they were able to find it for themselves, but soon
there would not be enough to find. And they were not yet able
to fly long distances. The solution to this problem might seem a
strange, and even a heartless, one, but there was no alternative.
The parent birds must go and leave what food remained for their
young.

All over the tundra this solution was being faced and accepted.
Other turnstones and black-bellied plovers, phalaropes, and knots

were beginning to go. As soon as she was sure that her young were able to fly, Calico raised her wings and headed south. She had no idea whether she would ever see her family again. It was likely that, somewhere along the long way back, Checkerback would overtake her. He was a strong flier and she was not. But the very fact that she was not, increased the chances that she might not survive to meet him. In any case, her instinct told her it was time to go, and off she went.

Checkerback stayed with his brood for another week, leading them to wet places to feed and bathe, standing guard and protecting them from their foes. Then, one morning, he too was gone.

It was now the end of July, and the young turnstones were left alone on the vast treeless plain. The chances that they would see their parents again were slight indeed. So were the chances that they would all make their way safely to that distant Brazilian beach. Far less than half of the birds that are hatched on the wild tundra survive to make the return journey.

Untold numbers of young birds are lost in one way or another every year. This is expected; it is why most birds lay more than one egg. It is even to be hoped for. If every egg laid was successfully hatched and produced a bird that grew to maturity, the world would be overrun with birds it could not support, and would become a rather unpleasant and frightening place.

Just as ecological balance demands that not all young birds survive, it also demands that the parents leave the young behind rather than stay and compete with them for the diminishing food supply.

It is a temptation to endow animals with human emotions and human reactions. It is a particular temptation because they so often appear to have them. Since no man has ever been a bird, or not that he can specifically recall, man does not actually know with certainty that birds do not react psychologically. To most observers, however, it seems logical and realistic to assume that they do not. When we call cowbirds "lazy" or blue jays "greedy" or vultures "disgusting," we are simply judging them by our own standards of behavior, and disregarding their avian instincts which are governed entirely by their physical needs.

As the sun swung lower every day along the flat horizon and light and twilight lessened, the few remaining adult birds looked lost and lonely. The young of many species began to move restlessly around in flocks, dropping down on low patches of Alpine bearberry as well as on kelp-strewn beaches, eating voraciously and building up a layer of protective fat. It was as if they sensed that snow and ice might at any time begin to cover whatever was left to eat. During the course of such intent feeding in a patch of bearberry, one of Checkerback's fledglings was carried off by a skua.

The big bird with the hooked beak had been sitting on an "owl stone," the rounded lookout perch usually occupied by a snowy owl. The stone was covered with a lacy pattern of orange-red lichen, resembling windowpane frost designs made of tomato juice.

The other young turnstones were ready to go. Their inherent powers of orientation, their innate navigational skills, their built-in compass sense—whatever it was that guided them would start them on their way to their destinations. They left the familiar shores of the only home they had ever known and headed out over the open sea. They were embarked on their first long journey.

"Big Wind Comin'"

WEEKS BEFORE his young left their tundra home, Checkerback had traveled as far south as Nova Scotia. The urge to migrate south was not as strong a compulsion as had been the need to journey north; it was a far more leisurely trip. Mating, and rearing and defending young had been accomplished; the days were not yet cold; his wintering grounds would be warm and sunny when he reached them. Banded turnstones have been reported to travel as far as four hundred and fifty miles in a day, or a night. But Checkerback was in no hurry.

On a wooded island guarding the entrance to Mahone Bay he rested for a day or two, eating the wild cranberries and huckle-berries. The island was called Ironbound, because on the Atlantic side the high cliffs were banded with an ore that looked like rusted iron. On a grassy knoll surrounded by wind-bent firs and spindly spruces stood a lighthouse.

Under the roots of the firs and spruces, birds called Leach's petrels had dug burrows. In them they laid their eggs and raised their young. And often at night they would come out to dart and dip like bats around the light, twittering softly and squeaking. The name "petrel" is said by some to come from Peter, the disciple. When they fly close to the water, fishing, the birds give the appearance of walking on the waves. To mariners they are often known as "stormy petrels" and are believed to foretell bad weather when they gather at sea. Actually these petrels spend much of their time on land, in their burrows beneath the grizzled trees which, like the live oaks on the southern sea islands, are bearded with a kind of hanging moss.

Petrels dig their holes with remarkable rapidity, using both their bills and their feet. An odd musky odor hangs around the entrances to these burrows which are also nests; the birds spray it forth when they sense approaching danger, and thus inadvertently lead the intruder straight to their doors.

But these little gray birds also travel miles and miles from their underground homes, ranging the open sea in every kind of weather, feeding on the small fish and crustaceans swimming near the surface. Sometimes they will alight on the water and swim with their wings held daintily over their backs. The fishermen on Ironbound call them "Mother Carey's Chickens," or "Careys" for short.

The fishermen on that remote rocky island called Ironbound have many stories to tell. One is about a neighboring island, even farther out to sea, where the lighthouse keeper is the only human inhabitant. Not long ago, as time is counted on an island, the keeper disappeared. His table was set for breakfast; coffee and toast, smoked mackerel and cream were laid out. But his gun and his skiff were gone. Only when the light did not flash on that night

did anyone know that something was wrong. The fishermen guess that he saw a raft of "sheldrake" floating in the surf above the reef, and that he left the table to try to bring down a brace of mergansers for dinner.

The same fishermen also tell tales of Captain Kidd. In the very bay where the Ironbound light stands sentinel, but far closer to shore, lies an island named for the graceful arching oaks that grow there. Oak Island has a natural half-moon harbor, the horns extended by a curve of rocks on either end of the crescent in a kind of breakwater.

There are those who believe that this breakwater is not as natural as the harbor itself is; that it was, in fact, constructed later by pirates. They go on to say that these pirates belonged to the band of Captain William Kidd, the minister's son who turned from pirate hunting to piracy.

Part of Kidd's famous treasure was found off Long Island, but not all of the treasure by any means. And an "authentick" map has indicated to a great many treasure seekers that the rest may still lie buried on Oak Island.

That this is considered a good deal more than a fisherman's myth is borne out by the astonishing fact that thousands of dollars have been more or less literally sunk in the digging operations on the island. With machinery that Captain Kidd could never have

dreamed of, let alone been able to use, shafts seeking for gold have been sunk all over Oak Island. And when the water rushes into one shaft, flooding it, another shaft is begun until the island has become honeycombed with them, much as, in another way, the petrels with their burrows are honeycombing the earth under the Ironbound spruces.

And so Checkerback continued on his homeward journey. Down the rocky Atlantic coast the lighthouses stood like giant candles. Most of them were automatic now, turned on and off by electric timers. Many of the small adjoining or nearby houses had been abandoned; a lighthouse life is a lonely life. But around the empty buildings some asters and chrysanthemums still blossomed in the fall to testify that once a keeper and his wife polished the great magnifying lens and with a kitchen match lit the tip of the wick rising from its snakelike coil in a bath of kerosene.

Lighthouses have come a long way since the days of chrysanthemums and kitchen matches. In 1833 a revolutionary openwork iron lighthouse was erected on a sandy shoal in the Thames estuary. This solved the problem of what to do in a place where a light was badly needed but the ground was unstable, with shifting sands or crumbling reefs. Lightships, an earlier experiment, had a way of changing their locations by dragging anchor in the current, or being blown off position by the wind. The octagonal conelike skeleton tower of Alligator Light, off Florida's Indian Key, was inspired by the Thames lighthouse.

Alligator Light was named for Alligator Reef which in turn had received its name from the schooner *Alligator,* Commodore David Porter's pirate-fighting ship which sank in the rough waters above the reef in 1822, to the delight of all pirates. It was the same David Porter who remarked of another light: "Hatteras, the most important on our coast is, without doubt, the worst light in the world . . . When I did see it, I could not tell it from a steamer's light, excepting that the steamer's lights are much brighter."

During the Labor Day hurricane of 1935, the keeper of the Alligator Reef Light saw in the gleam of his lamp a towering wave bearing down on him. He leaped for a ladder and clung to it. When the sun broke through the tearing clouds the next day, it shone on the Alligator's broken lens glittering on a beach eight miles away.

And in a hurricane called Donna, in 1960, four Coast Guardsmen were ordered to remain on Alligator Reef throughout the night. In spite of extensive storm warnings, there were ships nearby and in danger. The light must be manned in case flying surf shut off the electricity. The lighthouse swayed and creaked throughout the gale; the terrified occupants clung to the supports. But by the light of dawn when they looked across at the devastated shore, they wondered whether they might not, after all, be the only survivors of the storm.

The word "hurricane" is believed to have originated, aptly enough, in the stormy West Indies. The Carib Indians called great winds *huracans*. And the Mayan Indians of Guatemala in Central America worshiped a god named *Hunrakan,* "The Heart of the Sky." He was the god of stormy weather, and the Indians carved him in their temple decorations, ornamented with snakelike spirals and coils, the very twistings of a cyclone.

Naturally enough the Indians, like the natives of all the West Indian islands, lived in great fear of hurricanes. They did not understand their origins and causes, and believed that they must be manifestations of the wrath of Hunrakan whom they had unwittingly displeased. To this day in some of the islands the children sing:

> "Big wind comin',
> Skies are scowlin',
> Hear it howlin',
> Big wind comin' this way."

Along with their fear, they cherish their superstitions too. Most

of these have to do with animals. On the Keys some people still believe in animal portents. They say it is a sure sign of an impending hurricane when land crabs leave their mangrove jungles and scuttle down the Overseas Highway looking for high ground, dogs bark restlessly and cats inch along fencetops and climb trees, sea birds move inland and insects invade a house. The Seminole Indians say that when the saw grass blooms in the Everglades it is time to seek drier land. Since the saw grass blooms in the late summer and fall, hurricane time, they are wise to move.

The West Indians have a saying that they recite about hurricanes. "June, too soon; July, stand by; August, it must; September, remember; October, all over." Actually they are about a month ahead of themselves. September is more apt to be a hurricane month than August, and it is not until well into November that the danger from the big wind is presumed to be over.

Many hurricanes originate in the southeast Atlantic, near the Cape Verde Islands and the Sargasso Sea. In that relatively windless area called the doldrums, the hot summer air rises from the warm placid water. As the air rises it is cooled and condensation forms, rising in towering clouds, and churning around a center, or eye, of calm. These hollow cones of wind and water swirl in a counterclockwise motion north of the equator, given their forward impetus, like a spinning top, by the direction of the earth's rotation.

In spite of the tremendous speed of hurricane winds—at least

seventy-five miles per hour to be termed a hurricane at all, and with gusts over twice as high—the storms themselves move slowly. With radar, and weather reconnaissance planes, and satellites, the Hurricane Warning Service of the United States Weather Bureau is able to forecast and track the storms, preventing widespread loss of life and minimizing property damage.

This, however, has not always been the case. A few centuries ago hurricanes took people by surprise. In fact, they have changed the course of history.

During the hundred years between 1500 and 1600, the Spanish court estimated that it had lost—in American equivalence—two millions dollars worth of gold and precious stones, part of the loot from Montezuma's palace. The treasure lay on the coral and sand beneath the Gulf Stream, the Spaniards' ocean river passage home. Hurricanes had sunk the cumbersome galleons of the Plate Fleet. The Armada had been defeated by winds as well as by Sir Francis Drake and Sir John Hawkins; Spain's fortunes were on the wane. In 1763 *Terra Florida* was ceded to England.

Before that, a hurricane had already changed Florida's fate. In 1565, a French fleet led by Jean Ribaut, attempting to seize the Spanish settlement at St. Augustine, was swept down the coast and onto out-jutting Cape Canaveral by hurricane winds. The Spaniards believed that only the storm had kept Ribaut, with his superior

forces, from capturing their village and claiming the country for France.

Hurricanes affect more than history; they alter the very contours of the land, and its ecology. They have been called the world's great distributors. By air and water they have carried birds and butterflies, snails and raccoons and frogs, and the seeds of delicate orchids and massive mahoganies to new homes. They have spread seaweed to fertilize the soil. They have destroyed and restored coastlines. When one realizes that an hour of hurricane energy equals more than all of the electricity generated in the United States for a year, one has to realize that there is practically nothing that a hurricane cannot do.

A long lead-colored swell like an unbroken wave rolled in from the east. The sky had a curiously brassy look; high feathery clouds reaching up in a V from the horizon were edged in orange. Checkerback, the ruddy turnstone, migrating south, flew in above the long swell and dropped down on the parade ground of an old island fort—Fort Jefferson, on Garden Key in the Dry Tortugas.

Hummingbirds fluttered in the Geiger trees. Noddy and sooty terns wheeled like butterflies above the roofless parapets. A damaging hurricane in 1918 had swept away what remained of the rooftops.

Checkerback had been there before. With other turnstones he milled about uncertainly, tired from his long journey and nervous about the approaching storm. In his porous bones he could feel the lowering pressure. And he had not been able to find Calico.

There was always the possibility that some of the females of the flock might still be ahead of the males on their journey. In Calico's case this possibility was no longer valid. She had reached the coast of Maine but no further.

It had been a cool and foggy evening. Shreds of mist and drifting fog had confused the little flock she was traveling with, giving everything a vagueness. The landscape seemed obscured; the sharp outlines of the firs and spruces were softened and blunted beyond recognition. Ocher-colored seaweed, bladder wrack and brown algae, lay spread out on the rocks at low tide like limp hair. Cruising gulls glowed white against a world that seemed totally gray.

Calico had been exhausted. Never a strong flier, keeping up with her flock had strained her endurance. She fluttered down onto a ridge of rock that had been tilted, geologists say, sixty million years ago. It gave the ridge the appearance of frayed cloth, fringed and wrinkled.

Over it once had towered the spar pines, straight trunks used for the masts of sailing ships. There was no harbor in the world, ship-builders said, where Maine pines had not cast their shadows, no port too far for the spar pines. Now the trees on the foggy promontory were wind-bent and low, and the clipper ships were gone.

The automatic light on the point flashed on as darkness settled. As if on one impulse, the birds took off. Some of them crashed blindly headfirst into the light.

A few of them were merely stunned. In an hour or even less they would be up again and on their way. But Calico would not be going with them. Checkerback's mate lay on the cement step at the lighthouse door; her neck was broken.

Ponce de León, who discovered the Tortugas, named them for the sea turtles he found on the beach. That was in 1513, when turtles in great quantities pulled themselves ashore to lay their eggs in the sand unmolested by marauding mammals. Afterwards sailors added the word "Dry" to the island group because they were able to find no wells to give them drinking water.

One of the Tortugas was called Garden Key, and on it the United States government built one of its first lighthouses in 1825. Twenty-one years later a red brick fortress was begun for the protection of the southernmost part of the country. It was named Fort Jefferson, and its hexagonal walls that surrounded sixteen acres, almost all of Garden Key, included the graceful light. For thirty years the construction continued, at a cost of three million

dollars, with parapets fifty feet high and eight feet thick above a moat. It was intended to house fifteen hundred enlisted men and officers, and four hundred and fifty guns. But it never heard a shot fired in anger. And it was never finished. Held by the North during the Civil War, it was turned into a prison; the moat is said to have been infested with barracudas and sharks. And there in 1865 came its most noted prisoner, Dr. Samuel Mudd.

Dr. Mudd, by one of those chance quirks of fate, happened to be the physician who set the broken leg of the man who assassinated Lincoln. Sentenced to life imprisonment because of this act which was considered traitorous, he skillfully treated victims of a yellow-fever epidemic. After four years of wind and sun and fever, he was exonerated and set free, but not before he became part of our vocabulary. The expression "Your name is Mudd," however it may be spelled, still refers to the unfortunate doctor.

The fort, once called the "Gibraltar of the Caribbean," was abandoned in 1874 to become the "Ghost of the Gulf." But the terns did not abandon it, nor did egg hunters, smugglers, rum-runners, and wandering fishermen and shrimpers. Today the fort is a national monument and the birds are protected. At the rookery on nearby Bush Key the noddies and sooties have been nesting for over one hundred years, and shading their eggs from the hot April sun, rather than the customary heating or incubation. Now 142

Bush Key is visited mainly by ornithologists, engaged in banding and keeping count of the thousands of birds.

Checkerback, crouching with his companions at the base of the old lighthouse, felt the full violence of the September hurricane sweep over him. Winds blew marbles of surf across the empty parade ground; the rain scudded under the open arches and flooded the moat. A moment of calm arrived: the wind fell and the sun shone from a bright blue sky down a white whirling cone of clouds. The turnstones felt the warmth of the sun and crept out on the bricks to dry their feathers. Some of them, warmed and dried, even attempted to continue their migration.

But hurricanes were not new to Checkerback. He had been in another, the autumn before, on Martinique. He understood that the eye, the center of the storm, would pass and that the winds would blow again. He looked up into the cone and saw terns spinning round and round against the blue sky and the wall of clouds. And he huddled against the old bricks, in the shelter of the Ghost of the Gulf, and waited for the hurricane to pass.

"*Adieu Madras*"

FROM EARLIEST TIMES men have been fascinated by birds, and envied them, and longed to share their ability to fly. Some have even tried. The Latin poet Ovid, compiling his Greek mythology during the reign of Caesar Augustus, recounts the story of Daedalus and Icarus.

Mythology, too, is full of bird stories, and each of the major gods and goddesses had a particular one that was sacred to him. Jupiter's was the eagle, Juno's the peacock, Minerva's the owl, Venus' the dove, and Mars's the vulture. Jupiter, or Zeus, is depicted coming to earth in the form of a swan to court the fair Leda.

The ancient Greeks and Romans were not the only people who worshiped birds. To the early Egyptians any bird symbolized the immortal soul.

Identifiable birds in paleolithic cave paintings, etched and colored on underground rock walls more than one hundred centuries ago in Spain and France, testify to Stone-Age man's interest in birds, and his belief that they possessed supernatural powers.

American Indians carved significant birds on their totem poles, often the thunderbird which they believed brought thunder. They wore feathers in their ceremonial dances, hoping that the feathers would endow them with wondrous powers. The dances themselves imitated the strutting and flapping behavior of birds, and were named Crane Dance or Crow Dance. Mayan Indians in Central

145

America held the quetzal sacred, and only rulers and holy men were allowed to wear its long emerald-green plumes.

Why did primitive man worship birds? The most obvious reason seems to be that birds, arriving from the sky or high places, the domain of most gods, were considered holy messengers, and therefore imbued with deity themselves. Ovid wrote of the belief that "those who could traverse the air were gods."

That birds were at home in the high reaches of the upper air filled men with awe as well as envy. Then too, birds appeared to have certain human characteristics: they walked on two legs; they danced and sang; and they built shelters for their young. Finally, many of them were dazzlingly beautiful, with iridescent colors in breathtaking combinations. In any case, bird worship is almost as old as man himself.

Through the years, birds have played their role in history. Everyone knows of the dove that brought Noah a bit of olive branch to indicate that the flood was over and the world once again safe to live in. Birds first informed Columbus that he was nearing land. "All night they heard birds passing," he wrote in his journal on October 9, 1492.

Four nights before, on October 5, there had been a full moon   146

in a cloudless sky. Columbus' men, discouraged and mutinous, looked up from the decks where they were trying to sleep, and saw flocks of tiny land birds passing over the face of the moon. Columbus saw them too. The birds—thrushes, warblers, and vireos on their autumnal migration—were taking the shortest route, west-southwest, from the eastern coastline of the nearby continent to what would one day be called the West Indies. Almost on a whim, Columbus altered his course and followed them. And they led him to his first landfall, changing not only his course but the course of history.

Thousands of miles from the High Arctic where he had spent the summer, Checkerback, the ruddy turnstone, dropped down on the black sand beach of Martinique. The pale water lapped as gently as it had six months before, and the Caribbean Sea lay flat and glassy. On the beach the tall palms stood motionless, but underneath them on the sand, broken fronds and bent-over trunks showed that Martinique had not escaped the hurricane that had trapped Checkerback and his flock in the Dry Tortugas. Smashed coconut shells lay everywhere. In the hills and *mornes* leading up to Mount Pelée, branches were strewn where the trees had flowered. Only the treeless volcano looked untouched, brooding down over the island.

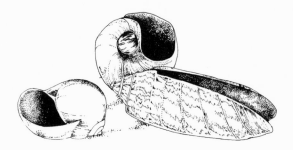

Well away from the storm, the shorebirds spread out on the warm beaches and basked in a heat that they had not known for months. The flocks were not as concentrated as they had been; many birds had dropped out along the way. Some had been lost, as Calico had, by flying into tall buildings, lighthouses, and other obstacles—even a bat tower. Some had drowned while crossing long passages of open water; others had not survived the buffeting of gale and hurricane winds.

Many of the birds had lingered behind on the mud flats and marshes of the Carolina coastline or the shell beaches of Georgia islands where they had found the foraging good. The great urgency of the northward migration was over; they had time to spend in the warmth of the sun. The wintering grounds would be there for them when they arrived. And mating and nest building and the rearing of young was over for another year.

Checkerback had momentarily given up looking for Calico. There was still, for him, the chance that she might be waiting on a mangrove-bordered Brazilian beach. People never fail to marvel that birds recognize one another. To us every turnstone may look exactly alike. It is a temptation to suggest that to a turnstone every human being looks alike.

Along the docks in the busy noisy harbor of Fort-de-France, several interisland sloops had been sunk in the storm. There they still lay, on the bottom, gleaming up through the transparent water, 148 some even yet tied to their pilings. Sailors, as usual, were engaged in loading or unloading their cargoes, speaking softly in their French *patois,* laughing and lazing. They still sang from time to time, sometimes the colonial governor's love song, "Adieu Foulard, Adieu Madras," and the tall young girls, part French, part African, and part Indian, still glided by with fruit and flowers in baskets on their heads. They had long since forsaken the foulard and the madras.

Across the Savane the statute of the Empress Joséphine, eyes trained on her birthplace, had weathered the hurricane, as it had weathered many others. But several spindly palms had fallen around it, and these, like the sunken sloops, remained where they lay.

Checkerback flew to the island with a sense of recognition but no feeling of belonging. He had been there before and he would come again. For the moment, his migration nearly over, he was content to stay and rest for a while.

Idly he waddled along the beach, under the shadow of the volcano which now wore a smokelike plume of cloud at its peak, under the soaring tropic-birds and frigate-birds he went, under the sea-grape trees where he probed the rain-pitted sand for crustaceans, or for beetles blown by the storm. Away from his flock for a moment, he walked up to a black-bellied plover, and they stood side by side, looking out to sea. The water and the air were warm; food was plentiful; the birds were rested.

In the constant flow of birds coming and birds going, rising and

settling, wings aslant and glistening in the tropical light, the plover
wheeled and was gone. The ruddy turnstone stood where he was,
like a burnished bit of driftwood on the sand. Then he rejoined his
flock. In the morning, or in a week or two, Checkerback would
set out again on his long journey.

List of Illustrations

Pages

13 Ruddy Turnstone
14 Limulus
16 American Jaçana
17 *left to right:* American Oystercatcher, a drawing after a plate by John James Audubon; Spotted Sandpiper, a drawing after a plate by John James Audubon
18 Ruddy Turnstone
19 Black-bellied Plovers
20 *left to right:* Florida Fighting Conch; Netted Olive; Coquina
21 Ruddy Turnstone
22 Bananaquit
23 Magnificent Frigate-Birds
24 Ruddy Turnstone
25 Bee Hummingbird
27 Ruddy Turnstone
29 Ruddy Turnstone
30 Ruddy Turnstones
33 Green Turtle
34 *left to right:* Cowrie, Northern Moon Snail; Shark Eye; Lettered Olive
35 *top to bottom:* Virginia Oyster; Ponderous Ark
36 Black-bellied Plovers
38 *top to bottom:* Ruddy Turnstone, a drawing after a plate by John James Audubon; Great White Heron, a drawing after a plate by John James Audubon
41 Ruddy Turnstone
42 *top:* Ruddy Turnstone. *bottom, left to right:* Gulf Periwinkle; Turkey Wing

Pages

43 Razor Clam
44 Willets, a drawing after a plate by John James Audubon
46 *top, left to right:* Razor Clam; Virginia Oyster; *bottom, left to right:* Northern Moon Snail; Shark Eye; Lettered Olive; Ponderous Ark
47 *left to right:* Turkey Wing; Gulf Periwinkle; Cowrie
48 Greater Yellowlegs
50 Mistletoe
51 Ruddy Turnstone
53 Ruddy Turnstone
54 *top:* Ruddy Turnstone; *bottom, left to right:* Northern Moon Snail; Shark Eye; Lettered Olive
55 *left to right:* Turkey Wing; Gulf Periwinkle; Cowrie
56 Ruddy Turnstone
57 Ruddy Turnstones
58 Dogwood
59 Dogwood
60 Limulus
61 *Archaeopteryx*
62–63 Hoatzin
64 *Archaeopteryx*
67 Ruddy Turnstone
69 *top to bottom:* Louisiana Heron, a drawing after a plate by John James Audubon; Little Blue Heron, a drawing after a plate by John James Audubon
70–71 Carolina Paroquet, a drawing after a plate by John James Audubon

Pages

73 Whooping Crane
74 Short-billed Marsh Wren
75 Ruddy Turnstone
76 Barred Owl, a drawing after a plate by John James Audubon
78 Ruddy Turnstones
79 Ruddy Turnstones
80 Mallard
81 *top to bottom:* Mute Swan; Fish Hawk, a drawing after a plate by John James Audubon
82 *left to right:* Northern Moon Snail; Shark Eye; Lettered Olive
83 *left to right:* Virginia Oyster; Ponderous Ark
85 Black-bellied Plovers
86 Red-tailed Hawk
87 Spruce Grouse
89 Ruddy Turnstone
91 Spotted Sandpiper, a drawing after a plate by John James Audubon
93 Green Turtle
94 Ruddy Turnstone
96–97 White Stork
98–99 Whooping Crane
100–101 Ruddy Turnstone
103 Barred Owl, a drawing after a plate by John James Audubon
104–5 Tree Sparrow
106 Swainson's Hawk, a drawing after a plate by John James Audubon
107 American Goshawk
109 Ruddy Turnstones
110–11 Tree Sparrows

Pages

112 Ruddy Turnstone
114 Ruddy Turnstone
115 Barred Owl, a drawing after a plate by John James Audubon
116–17 Ptarmigan
119 American Pipit
121 Ruddy Turnstone
122 Ruddy Turnstone
123 Ruddy Turnstone
124 Ruddy Turnstones
125 Ruddy Turnstone
126 *left to right:* Wilson's Phalarope; Knot, a drawing after a plate by John James Audubon
128–29 Great Skua
131 Leach's Petrel, a drawing after a plate by John James Audubon
133 American Merganser, a drawing after a plate by John James Audubon
134 Ruddy Turnstone
137 Ruddy Turnstone
138–39 Ruddy Turnstones
140 Ruddy Turnstone
142 Noddy Tern and chick
143 Sooty Tern
144 Griffon Vulture
146 Turkish Turtle Dove
147 Olive branch
148 *top:* Ruddy Turnstone; *bottom, left to right:* Northern Moon Snail; Shark Eye; Lettered Olive
149 Cowrie
150 Ruddy Turnstone

Index

Ailsa Craig, 66
alewives, 100
Alligator, Chief, 39
Alligator (schooner), 135
Alligator Light, 135
Anderson, Robert, 64
Aphrodite, 46
arbres à la pluie, 24–25
Archaeopteryx, 61–63
Arctic, 41–42, 113–30
Arctic foxes, 117, 124
Arctic grouse, 80
Arctic terns, 77, 107
Ardea occidentalis, 39
"*Arenaria interpres,*" defined, 14
Arenaria melanocephala, 17–18
Aristotle, 98–99
Artemis, 70
Ascension Island, 100
Atlantis, 34
Audubon, John 37–39, 59, 103
Aurora borealis, 116
Australian muttonbird, 104
Aztecs, 35, 46, 72

Babylonians, 33, 51
Baltimore, Lord, 59
Baltimore, Md., 84
bananaquit, 21–23

banding, 102–4
Barren Grounds, 101
Bartram, John, 71
Bartram, William, 71
bats, 101
beach grass, 84
beach heather, 86
beaches, 53–57. *See also* specific
  places
Beauregard, Pierre G. T., 64
Beebe, Willima, 96
Big Pine Key, 43–44
bison, 101
black-bellied plovers, 17, 37, 44, 85,
  120
black-necked stilts, 60, 68
black skimmers, 74
black turnstone, 17–18
black-whiskered vireo, 24
Blake, William, 90
blue jays, 111
boat-tailed grackles, 68, 83
bobwhites, 111
British Isles, 36
Bush key, 142
butterflies, 100, 102–3
Byrd, William, 59

Caesar, Julius, 50

Canada geese, 108
Cape Cod, 76–77, 85–94
Cape Hatteras, 77–78, 135
Cape Verde Islands, 137
Capistrano, 111
cardinals, 111
Carib Indians, 21, 135
caribou, 101, 116, 117–18
Carolina, 61–75
Carolina paroquets, 71–72
Catesby, Mark, 58–59, 71, 72, 74
Catesby, Roger, 58
cave paintings, 144
Celts, 50
Charleston, S.C., 63–64
Chesapeake Bay, 80, 82, 83–85, 104
chimney swifts, 98
Christmas, 49, 50
Civil War, 64, 78, 142
climate, 79. *See also* specific places
club mosses, 68–70
Columbus, Christopher, 21, 34, 146–47
coon oysters, 75
corals, 42
Coriolis force, 105
courting, 121–24
Creek Indians, 53
Crete, 70

crows, 111
cypresses; cypress swamp, 33, 68–73

Dade, Francis Langhorn, 39
date palm, 51
Davis, Jefferson, 64
Delmarva peninsula, 80–85
Diana, 70
dinoflagellates, 31
doldrums, 137
Doubleday, Abner, 64
doves, 83, 146
Druids, 48, 50
Dry Tortugas, 108, 139, 141–43
ducks, 106, 118, 120
dune goldenrod, 86
dunlins, 120

eels, 101
eggs, 123–24, 127
egrets, 75
Egypt, 51, 144
emperor penguins, 80
England and the British Isles, 36, 52–53
English sparrows, 111
evening grosbeaks, 106
Everglades, 137

Fawkes, Guy, 58
feathers, 18, 20, 76
fer-de-lance, 25–26
fern tree, 26
ferns, 68–70
fiddler crabs, 75
Fiske, John, 34
Florida, 29–44, 138–39
flowering plants, 26–27, 124–25
flycatchers, 24
Fort-de-France, 15–16, 19–28
Fort Frederica, 52–53
Fort Jefferson, 139, 141–42
Fort McHenry, 84
Fort Sumter, 63–64
Franklin, Benjamin, 35
frigate birds, 22

Garden Key, 139–40, 141–42
geese, 106, 108, 120
Georgia, 45–60
gods and goddesses, 46, 48–50, 144.
   See also specific countries, gods
golden plover, 106–7
Grand Banks, 36
great white heron, 39
Greeks, 33–34, 46, 144
grouse, 80, 87, 110
Gulf Stream, 34–35, 138

gulls, 118
Gunpowder Plot, 58

Hatteras Island, 77–78, 135
hawks, 87, 106
Hercules, 49
hermit crabs, 47
Herodotus, 34
heron, 39, 103–4
herring fishermen, 95
High Arctic, 41–42, 119–30
Hilton, William, 71
hoatzin, 62
Homer, 97
"homing instinct," 105
homing pigeons, 105, 108
horned larks, 118
horseshoe crabs, 93
Housman, Jacob, 40–41
Hudsonia, 86
hummingbirds, 25
Hurakan, 136
hurricanes, 135–43

immortelle, 26–27
Indian Key, 36–41
Indians, 40–41, 49, 136–37, 144–45.
   See also specific groups
insects, 115, 124

Ironbound Island, 131–33
Isis, 51
ivory-billed woodpecker, 72

jacaranda, 26
jaegers, 124
Jamaica dogwood, 43
Jeremiah, 97
Job, 97
Josephine, Empress, 16
Juno, 144
Jupiter, 49, 144

Key deer, 44
Key, Francis Scott, 84–85
Key West, 29
Keys, Florida, 29–44, 35, 137
Kidd, Captain William, 133–34

Lapland longspurs, 118
Leach's petrels, 131–32
lemmings, 101–2, 115, 117
lighthouses, 132–36
lightships, 134–35
limestone, 42–43
Linnaeus, 45, 58
live oaks, 48
liverworts, 70

Madison, Dolley, 84
magnetic field, earth's, 105, 108
Mahone Bay, 131
Maine, 140–41
manchineel trees, 24
mangroves, 33, 70
man-o'-wars, 22
Mars, 144
marsh wrens, 68
Martinique, 13–28, 147–50
Massachusetts, Cape Cod, 76–77, 85–94
mating, 121–24
Maury, Matthew Fontaine, 34–35
Mayan Indians, 136, 144–45
Miami, 39
migration, 97–112. *See also* specific places
Miles River, 82
Minerva, 144
mistletoe, 50
mockingbirds, 83
mollusks, 46–47
monarch butterflies, 100
mongooses, 26
Monitor, the, 78
Montezuma, 35, 72, 138
moon, 107
moon jellies, 95

moon snail, 47
moose, 116
mourning doves, 83
Mudd, Dr. Samuel, 142
musk oxen, 116

night flights, 93–112
Noah, 146
noddy terns, 108
northern lights, 116
Nova Scotia, 131–34

Oak Island, 133–34
oaks, 48–49, 50–51
oceanography, 33–35, 95–97
Oglethorpe, James Edward, 52–53
Olaus Magnus, 98
Orkneys, the, 66
ospreys, 80
ovenbirds, 112
Ovid, 144, 146
owls, 80, 115, 116
oysters, 75, 83

palms, 51
paroquets, 71–72
passenger pigeons, 73
peeps, 36

Pelée, Mount (volcano), 13, 14–15,
   27, 149
penguins, 77, 80
Perrine, Dr. Henry, 41
Perrine (village), 41
petrels, 131–32
phoebes, 74, 103, 104
Phoenicia(ns), 34, 51–52
phoenix, 51
photography, 109–10
pigeons, 73, 105, 108
Pine Islands, 43–44
pipits, 118–19
plankton, 30–31, 95
plants, 56–57, 86–87. See also trees;
   specific places, plants
Pliny the Elder, 51, 98
plovers, 18, 106–7; black-bellied, 17,
   37, 44, 85, 120
polar bears, 115
Ponce de León, Juan, 26, 29, 35, 141
Porter, David, 135
poui, 26
ptarmigans, 80, 115, 116, 117
pterosaurs, 62
Ptolemy, 34

Quetzalcoatl, 46
quetzals, 72, 145

radar, 109
radios, 111
rails, 68
rain trees, 24–25
Randolph, John, 59
ravens, 116
red-bellied woodpeckers, 83
redhead ducks, 106
Redi, Francesco, 101
redpolls, 118, 119
red-winged blackbirds, 67–68
reindeer, 101
rhododendron, 125
Ribaut, Jean, 138–39
rice, 73–74
ringing, 103–4
robins, 111
rock ptarmigan, 115
Rosa rugosa, 86–87
roseate spoonbills, 72
ruffed grouse, 110
Ruffin, Edward, 64
rufous-headed yellow warbler, 24

St. Augustine, 37, 138–39
St. Kilda's, 66
St. Pierre, 15, 21
St. Simons Island, 45–60
salmon, 100

salt marshes, 66–68
salt-spray rose, 86–87
sand, 54–55, 90–91
sanderlings, 16, 85
sandpipers, 18, 36–37
Santee swamp, 71–73
Sargasso Sea, 34, 101, 137
Savannah, Ga., 52
saw grass, 137
Scotland, 65–66
sea-grape trees, 22
seals, 118
Seminole Indians, 137
Seminole Wars, 39
shells, 46–47
Shetlands, the, 66
shrimp, 29–30
skipjacks, 83
skuas, 124, 130
Smith, John, 84
snakes, 25–26
snow buntings, 80, 117, 119
snowy owls, 80, 115
sooty terns, 108
South Carolina, 61–75
Spaniards, 29, 35, 52–53, 138
Spanish moss, 45
sparrows, 111, 112
stars, 112

stilts, 18, 60, 68
swallows, 59, 111
swamps, 68–73
swans, 80, 104
symbiosis, 45

tagging, 103
temperature, 110–11, 114–15; birds', 76
Thoreau, Henry David, 88–89
thrushes, 111
thunderbird, 144
Tillands, Elias, 45
Tillandsia, 45
trees, 48–51. *See also* specific trees
tropic-bird, 22
tufted titmice, 83
tundra, 113–30
turkey vultures, 83
turtles, 33, 93, 94, 100, 141

Venus, 144

Walden Pond, 88
walruses, 118
War of 1812, 84–85
War of Jenkins's Ear, 52, 60
Washington, D.C., 84
weather, 79. *See also* specific places
West Indies, 136, 137, 147. *See also* Martinique
whales, 118
whippoorwills, 83
whistling swans, 104
whooping crane, 73
willets, 44, 85
winds, 109; hurricanes, 135–43

yellowthroats, 74
young, turnstone, 125–26, 127–30

zamia, 43

ABOUT THE AUTHOR

MARJORY BARTLETT SANGER has written a number of books on natural history and conservation, among them *Mangrove Island* and *Cypress Country* for World. A Wellesley graduate and formerly a staff writer for the Audubon Society, she is a member of the American Ornithologists' Union and of the Wilson Ornithological Society. She now lives in Winter Park, Florida.

ABOUT THE ARTIST

BETTY FRASER is a free-lance illustrator and a keen amateur naturalist. Among the many books she has illustrated is *The Spell of Chuchuchan* by Elfreida Read, published by World. She now lives in New York City, but she was born in Massachusetts and studied at the Rhode Island School of Design.

1   2   3   4   5   73   72   71   70   69